CU00701022

WILLIAM LLEWELLYN'S

SPORT SUPPLEMENT

Reference Guide

DISCLAIMER: This information was gathered from sources including textbooks, medical journals, and pharmaceutical reports. Neither the author nor publisher assumes any liability for the information presented in this text. This book is not intended to provide medical advice. The purpose of this reference book is only to provide a compendium of information for the reader, for entertainment purposes only. None of the information in this book is meant to be applied. Readers are advised that some of the substances described in this reference book may be prohibited or used only under a physician's care in certain jurisdictions. Readers should consult with appropriate medical authorities before using any related products and the proper legal authorities if unsure of the status of substances described herein.

Molecular Nutrition LLC, 5500 Military Trail, Ste. 22-308, Jupiter, FL 33458

www.mnbody.com

A Word from the Author

I want to thank you for purchasing the first edition of *William Llewellyn's SPORT SUPPLEMENT REFERENCE GUIDE*. The SSRG is an ingredient-based non-commercialized review of the most popular supplements promoted for increasing muscle mass, strength, endurance, and athletic performance (ergogenic supplements). A detailed description of each supplement is provided, along with an assessment of efficacious dosage levels, safety and side effects, and the clinical and empirical evidence in support of its use. The purpose of this book is to help readers identify those sport supplement products best suited for their individual requirements and goals.

While I have made every attempt to include the most relevant sport supplement ingredients, this market is very dynamic. New compounds are continuously introduced, and old ones regularly come in and out of popularity. If I've overlooked a supplement that is of interest to you, or any other detail for that matter, please let me know. In my experience, the best and most relevant work is community driven. I would greatly appreciate your suggestions, and be sure to take them into consideration when updating future editions. Please email comments to Bill@SportSupplementBook.com.

❖ *Acknowledgments* ❖

I would like to extend my appreciation to everyone that helped make this book a reality. A special thank you goes to my wife Catherine, who was responsible for the layout. She spent many late nights on the pages and cover, and also months keeping the office together while I was working on the text. This book definitely would not be here without her help. My assistant technical editor Shawn Wells was also an enormous help, not only with the technical aspects, but also keeping me in check when I was being too harsh or too soft on a particular supplement. I also want to thank the MN crew (Conor, Matt, Jonathan, Dustin, and Josh), for helping with the book and keeping our community strong. Lisa Coe, who has been our chief graphic designer from day one, also has my gratitude. To all of my industry friends — it is the good people like you that I've had the privilege to meet along the way that keep me in this business when I'm ready to pack it in and sell bait down in Key West.

Lastly, I especially want to thank you, the reader, and everyone that has supported my sports nutrition company **Molecular Nutrition** over the years. Without you I wouldn't have a company. I am ever grateful for your trust and support.

- William Llewellyn

Table of Contents

PART III: CONSUMER EMPOWERMENT

REFERENCES   167

Sport Supplement Industry

Introduction

The United States is a nation that deeply values body image and physical achievement. We can see this in many things, such as our lavishment of high profile athletes. Consistently, in fact, they are the highest paid in the world. We also provide lucrative modeling careers for some of our most attractive individuals. Photographs of the buff and beautiful are used to sell almost every type of consumer good imaginable. With all of this achievement and beauty surrounding us, it is only natural that the individual desire to look and perform better would become strongly American as well. About 40 million of us now belong to one of an estimated 26,000 fitness clubs across the country. From memberships, to clothes, to nutritional shakes, pills, and powders, we spend a lot of money pursuing our individual fitness goals. In a nation of consumerism, health and fitness has become big business.

This book specifically focuses on the market for sport supplement products. Ergogenic supplements (those promising to help us become bigger, stronger, faster, or more enduring) now generate a stunning 2.5 billions dollars per year in revenue in the United States alone. It is an industry with hundreds of manufacturers, and a seemingly endless list of products and promises. As all consumers learn very quickly, sometimes sports nutrition products deliver on these promises. Other times, however, they do not. I have had the pleasure, and admittedly at times downright frustration, to be a part of this industry for more than a decade now. I am a scientific researcher, a company owner, an avid consumer. I love my job. My position has granted me a very unique inside view of this industry. More than that, it has given me the tools necessary to critically evaluate this market. I've written this book to pass these tools along to you.

At the very core, sports nutrition is a field of science. It is, however, also a business. Furthermore, there is no approval process for sport nutrition products, and the government is far too busy to review every marketing claim. As a result, the science that drives this field is sometimes secondary to the drive for profits. I have come to understand this business very well. I have learned that there are many people in sports nutrition like me, which hold reverence for this scientific field. I've also run across many consummate business people, who care little about fitness, and view this only as a revenue generating market. I am saddened to say that some have found it an ample market to exploit. Americans want to look and feel better. This can be an easy thing to take advantage of, especially if nobody is really watching.

Consumers of sport supplement products are faced with an extremely challenging task — deciding who and what to trust. I am here to help. I intend to do this not by recommending specific companies and products, but by giving you the tools necessary to identify products of value on your own. There is a lot of noise in this market, many misinterpretations of science, and many unsubstantiated claims. This noise, however, can be muffled when you know what to listen for. Throughout this book I will bring you through the science behind each of the popular sport supplement ingredients, and let you know what people are really saying about them. You'll learn what works, at what dosage, and in what context. I trust that if you pay careful attention to the information presented in this book, you will not be a disappointed consumer. O.K., enough buildup. Let's get started so you can see what I'm talking about.

Sport Supplement Overview

DEFINING A SPORT SUPPLEMENT

I think a good place to start this book is to talk briefly about what exactly a sport supplement is. As its name suggests, a sport supplement is a natural product designed to help improve your performance in athletics, or increase the physical results from exercise. If you are weight training, a supplement is supposed to help you build more muscle, lift more weight, or push more reps and sets. If you are competing in a sport, you might buy a supplement because it promises to make you faster. Or maybe it will give you more endurance, allowing you to perform at peak level for a longer period of time. In short, a sport supplement is supposed to make you better at what you are doing, to bring you closer to your individual goals.

SUPPLEMENT ACT OF 1994 – EXPANDING THE INDUSTRY

I think back to how much has (and has not) changed since I was a teenager. The supplements themselves were different back then, but the marketing was very much the same. Companies promised you the world in their advertising. Pictures of enormous bodybuilders and accomplished athletes were all over the magazines, with quotes promising that supplement products helped them achieve their success. This early business spawned a full industry. Quite frankly, however, the variety of ingredients available back then was extremely small. Aside from proteins, there really wasn't much worth purchasing. Companies thrived on the fact that most of us would spend a few hundred dollars on things like "steroid replacements" before we learned this ourselves. When we did, the rule became: if it is strong enough to change your body, it's a drug. Supplements "couldn't" work. Over the years I had seen many heavily hyped up ingredients come and go, which only seemed to support this.

You may be asking if "supplements can't work" is a reasonable assessment today. The answer, thankfully, is no. In 1994, a supplement market that before had mainly been limited to vitamins, minerals, and proteins was drastically opened up. Congress passed the Dietary Supplement Health and Education Act, which redefined a supplement as a vitamin, mineral, herb, botanical, amino acid, or any dietary substance used to supplement the diet. It may also be a concentrate, metabolite, constituent, extract, or combination of such a substance. This is an extremely broad definition. The most important part is that last phrase "any dietary substance." This essentially means that any compound that can be found in the food supply may qualify, even if it is found there in extremely small amounts. In other words, if it is natural and not prohibited, we can probably sell it.

The legal framework provided by DSHEA has allowed the sport supplement market to grow much larger and more robust than it was 15-20 years ago. Researchers have been free to explore many aspects of supplement design that were far outside the scope of allowance before. Most importantly, we now have many dietary ingredients that actually do produce remarkably strong effects for natural products. For example, the concept of a steroid replacement, or at the very least a natural product that can produce short term gains in muscle size and strength, is no longer a fantasy. There are several very efficacious and "proven" products in fact, and many more promising new technologies. There are many more ingredients that can help increase anaerobic and aerobic endurance. Whatever your sport or area of physical activity, you can find products today that are very likely to help improve your performance.

A "HANDS OFF" MARKET

There are some other key aspects to this market that need to be discussed. Most fundamentally, there is no approval process for supplements. Companies are not required to establish the safety of their ingredients before market. While DSHEA gives manufacturing guidelines, it is ultimately the responsibility of the Food and Drug Administration to prove a supplement is unsafe before it can be pulled from commerce. The logic of this is fairly straightforward. If an ingredient can be found naturally in the food supply, people are already consuming it. Increasing the consumption of an existing dietary ingredient should have fairly low risk. With the exception of a handful of injury cases (although admittedly these have sometimes been very serious), this has proven to be a reasonable framework for defining a dietary supplement.

Manufacturers are also not required to prove the efficacy of their products under DSHEA. There is no product testing. While the FDA does occasionally approve health claims, it does so very rarely, and only after extensive investigation. Most advertising claims have been reviewed only by the manufacturers making them. Companies are required to display a disclaimer if certain statements "have not been evaluated by the Food and Drug Administration." This disclaimer can be found on virtually every sport supplement. Essentially, as long as a company doesn't push so far that they get the attention of the media, the Federal Trade Commission, or class action attorneys, they are on their own. This means that while there are many products of high efficacy in this market, there are also many not worth the cost of their packaging. The market has expanded, for both better and worse.

The Supplement Business

Scientists may develop sport supplement ingredients, but these ingredients are dosed, combined, packaged, and sold by profit-driven businesses. This is vitally important to remember at all times. Like all industries, there are many businesses that really care about the efficacy of their products, and many others concerned only with maximizing profits. Trying to figure out the difference as you review the various companies and products can seem like a daunting task. When a consumer can understand the nature of the business, however, it is much easier to navigate the market. To that end, this section will serve as a basic introduction to the supplement business, with a special emphasis on the strategies used by many companies to maximize profits.

The more aggressive companies tend to employ a number of strong marketing tactics to increase the perceived value of their products in the eyes of consumers. When applied, these can dramatically widen margins and increase sales. Buyers, however, might regard some of these tactics as questionable (some more than others). I will not cite examples, but can tell you I've seen extremes where $2 worth of ingredients would generate a $90 sale, on a product that delivers absolutely no value to the customer, making profits in the many millions of dollars. Thankfully, such extreme examples are uncommon. Still, even some of the more reputable companies may feel forced to apply some of these marketing tactics if they want to remain competitive. It is important to keep an eye out for them. Many of the more popular tactics are reviewed below.

MIXING INGREDIENTS

Most sports supplement products contain not one, but many ingredients. There is often a strong financial reason for mixing ingredients like this. When a partic-

ular supplement becomes widely available and desired by consumers, its price stabilizes at a reasonable low given its cost of production. In the industry, we call this type of ingredient a commodity. This is a very good thing for consumers. They get to save money. Companies, on the other hand, cannot maintain high margins doing this. While some businesses do focus on selling generic single-ingredient products at low margins and high volumes, most cannot work with this model. They sell their products through distributors, who sell them to stores, who sell them to consumers. For those keeping count, that is three businesses being sustained on the same products. Higher margins are absolutely necessary for most manufacturers to survive.

To separate their products from commodity-level pricing, companies may combine many ingredients into their own special formula. They will likely employ one or more truly "active" supplement ingredient(s) for efficacy. Creatine is a very good example of such an ingredient. A sports nutrition manufacturer can't make much money selling a pure creatine monohydrate product. Yet almost all of them sell some form of creatine. Most will mix creatine with two or more additional ingredients, and make marketing promises that this new version is far more effective. Don't get me wrong. There are many truly efficacious combinations; products that come together as a whole from many separate parts. Most other times, however, these ingredient mixtures amount to little more than low cost add-ons to impress the buyer. Consumers need to closely scrutinize all ingredients and dosages if they want to maximize the value of their purchases.

PROPRIETARY BLENDS

FDA regulations allow manufactures to hide the exact

amount of the non-nutritive ingredients in a product by combining them into a label item called a "proprietary blend". To comply with regulations, the ingredients must be listed in order of prevalence, and the total amount of the proprietary blend disclosed. The proprietary blend serves one of two purposes. The first is that it can hide the exact formula from competitors, making the product more difficult to copy. The second reason is to hide the exact amount of each ingredient from consumers, so they are unaware of what the product may be valued in comparison to other products with similar ingredients. With this in mind, consumers need to scrutinize these label entries even more closely if they want to determine the potential value of each product.

Provided the label is an accurate reflection of a product's ingredients, some simple mathematics can give us the high and low range for each ingredient in a proprietary blend. The minimum amount of the first ingredient is determined by dividing the total weight of the proprietary blend by the number of ingredients. On the high end, the blend may consist entirely of the first ingredient. The company could have added trace

levels of all remaining ingredients (the low end of the range). This is perfectly legal, in case you were wondering. The high-end of the range is calculated by dividing the total weight by the ingredient's position in the blend (1 for first, 2 for second, 3 for third etc.). This works because if any lower ingredient were present in a higher concentration, it would have to be higher on the list.

For the sake of example, the calculated ranges of all ingredients in a hypothetical proprietary blend called "MuscleMaxo" have been listed below. Each daily dosage contains 1,000 mg (combined) of 5 ingredients. If you divide the weight of the blend (1,000 mg) by the number of ingredients (5), you know that this product must contain at least 200 mg of creatine monohydrate. Any less than this, and it could not be the first thing listed in the blend. The product could also contain 1,000 mg of creatine monohydrate, and trace levels of the remaining ingredients. Even so, 1,000 mg is still too little to illicit a strong ergogenic effect. With the remaining ingredients, we see that they also are not present in dosages that have been proven efficacious.

MuscleMaxo 1,000 mg

A proprietary blend of creatine monohydrate, arginine ethyl ester, beta alanine, citrulline malate, and arachidonic acid.

Proprietary Blend Breakdown (*a mathematical examination*)

#	Ingredient	Low	High
1	Creatine monohydrate	200 mg	1,000 mg
2	arginine ethyl ester	0 (trace)	500 mg (1,000 divided by 2)
3	beta alanine	0 (trace)	333 mg (1,000 divided by 3)
4	citrulline malate	0 (trace)	250 mg (1,000 divided by 4)
5	arachidonic acid	0 (trace)	200 mg (1,000 divided by 5)

FANCY INGREDIENT NAMING

What's in a name? In the world of marketing, sometimes everything. Consumers often search out the latest and greatest. They don't want the "same old stuff". So what do you do when all you have is the same old stuff? You can spice up your labels by calling the ingredients by new trademark names. For example, a company might think creatine monohydrate is too plain. After all, everybody knows creatine. Instead, they might call theirs "Cellular Nano-Intensified Conversion-Enhanced Creatine Monohydrate". This sounds extremely high tech, doesn't it? Of course, this name means exactly nothing. The only thing different about this creatine monohydrate is what they call it. Fancy naming like this is a common practice with sport supplement products. Just remember to ignore these trademarks and identify exactly what each ingredient really is, and you shouldn't go wrong.

THE "LATEST AND GREATEST"

This is an industry of innovation. Stores and consumers alike love new products. A company can make a lot of money introducing new ingredients the market has never seen before. This is especially true if you can create good stories about what they are, where they came from, and what they do. Even if they are completely worthless, it doesn't matter. Only the way you market them matters. This bold boast seems a lot more reasonable when you put it into perspective. There is always some lag between the time a new ingredient is released and hyped up, and the time consumers really understand its potential, real or imagined. A lot of product can be sold in this time. A story can indeed be as profitable as true innovation, perhaps more, as it costs a lot less to write a story than it does to legitimately develop and study an effective new ergogenic supplement. Scrutinize every ingredient. Be especially cautions if you cannot find reputable studies to support the use of something you are unfamiliar with.

WEIRD SCIENCE

Since sports nutrition, at its core, is a field of science, consumers tend to be very receptive to a scientific message. They are usually looking for products developed by scientists, which contain effective ingredients that have been validated both in the laboratory and in the real world. Knowing this, supplement manufacturers often promote their products with advertising that appears to be highly scientific. They may reference medical studies, cite clear statistics and figures about what it has been "proven" to do, and use detailed biological diagrams to get the message "this is scientific" across. Sometimes these messages are very accurate, and reflect the true academic work that went in to developing a product. At other times, however, it may amount to little more than creative marketing.

There are many ways to misrepresent science for the sake of advertising. For example, in some cases the smallest pieces of information are blown way out of proportion. Let's say there was a study showing that a particular nutrient produced a 10% increase in testosterone when given to rats in high doses. For the researchers, this was only a preliminary investigation. It may not mean anything for humans, and they'd never make claims about such use. But to a savvy supplement manufacturer, this was the "biggest breakthrough in sport supplement history". A small preliminary study result, which may not even relate to humans, is misrepresented as a "scientifically proven supplement for double digit testosterone increases".

Sometimes companies won't bother trying to misrepresent the data from a medical paper. Instead, they will simply fabricate figures that look even better. For example, let's say that a company owner notices that their competitor is promising a 100% increase in testosterone with their product. Maybe it is based on misrepresented animal study data, as we just discussed. Now this second manufacturer is more aggressive. They might counter their competition by saying that their product produces a 1,000% increase in testosterone, ten times better. To support this, they might fabricate graphs, measurements, subjects, even full "in-house studies". In reality, however, they are just trying to make a stronger claim than the competition, to get more business than the competition. These figures are not based on anything real.

One of the best marketing tools in this industry is an official clinical study proving your particular product works. Clinical studies, however, can be very expensive. The threshold for statistical proof is also very high, and often not easily reached. It can be a risky endeavor to try and validate a product with a real independent study. There are other options, though. It is not impossible to find scientists willing to produce favorable studies for pay. They may use protocols that are partial to one outcome, such as manipulating the makeup of the groups or substituting the supplement for a drug. They may simply miscalculate the raw data. These studies are of no scientific value, and are not commonly published in reputable peer-reviewed journals. They look extremely official though, with graphs, percentages, and a PhD title next to the author's name. Always find out if a study was actually published, and more importantly, where.

Lastly, sometimes the illusion of scientific development is all a company needs. I had a conversation with a marketing consultant a few weeks ago. I was explaining a detailed clinical study that my company had funded, and the promising results it returned. When I mentioned it was very expensive, he chuckled. He told me, "Look at (name withheld). They are one of the best selling companies in the industry. Their entire image is scientific, and they have not funded a single clinical study. Your study is great, but instead of "clinically proven" you could have just called your product "scientifically formulated", put a picture of a guy in a lab coat in your ads, and given

the same impression without the cost". So true. Remember to look closely. Separate scientific substance from marketing illusion.

EXCEPTIONAL CLAIMS IN ADVERTISING

The famous author and astronomer Carl Sagan once said, "Extraordinary claims require extraordinary evidence". At times, however, the sports nutrition industry appears to be one small corner of the universe where this rule doesn't apply. Many supplement manufacturers routinely make outrageous claims in their advertising, often with a complete lack of support. As discussed before, the supplement market is not closely regulated or monitored by the government. Because of this, exceptional claims have become an accepted fact of the industry. The aggressive companies, which make the boldest claims, often get ahead the fastest. I was once told, "if you are not prepared to push the limits of advertising, you should not expect to sell more product than companies that are". It is that true and that simple. Remember, it is all advertising. Consumers need to critically analyze all claims, and draw conclusions based only on what is proven.

BEFORE AND AFTER PICTURES

Comparison pictures showing what someone looked like before the use of a sport supplement, and how their body has changed as a result, are very common in this industry. The "before and after" picture set usually represents a substantial body transformation. In some cases, these before and after photos are real, and reflect tangible benefits that were received from a product. In other cases, however, these photos may have been manipulated to look more dramatic. How does one tell the difference? There is no easy answer. Even to the trained eye, it can be difficult, of not impossible, to know for sure if a set of before and after pictures is a true reflection of the effect of a supplement, or simply aggressive and creative marketing.

Manipulating before and after pictures is fairly easy. For example, you can use bad lighting, relaxed stomach muscles, pale skin, and frowning to make the "before" photo look unappealing. The after photo would have studio lighting, tensed abdominal muscles, rub-on-tan, and a wide smile. I was interviewed for a film a couple of years ago called *Bigger, Stronger, Faster*. They show an excellent scene where an impressive set of before and after pictures were taken *on the very same day*. I've also seen very old pictures with false dates used as the before shots. I've known models to run heavy steroid cycles in preparation for an after shoot. I even witnessed a company blatantly edit their advertising pictures. The arms of one model were widened, a more defined cut was made in the triceps, the waistline was taken in, and someone else's abdominals were even placed on top of the model's! Yes, it really does happen.

ENDORSEMENTS

Many supplement companies use celebrity endorsements to sell their products. This is especially common with professional bodybuilders, wrestlers, and fighters. The ideal image of an endorsement is a sports figure making remarkable success because of a specific supplement product, and working with the company to endorse it because the supplement worked so well for them. The reality, however, is often very different. While I can't speak about any situation in particular, I can tell you how endorsements work from the inside. Living life as a professional athlete is expensive. Sports, bodybuilding especially, usually do not pay very well. Endorsement contracts are the bread and butter for many professionals. This alone is important to consider.

Athletes will often work hard on their career for many years before they become high profile enough to ob-

tain endorsement money. When that day comes, the athlete will shop around in search of a contract. A cynic would automatically conclude that the best offer, not the best product, gets the endorsement. A friend of mine has a good story about endorsements. He recently spoke with a professional bodybuilder that is under contract with a major supplement company. He told my friend that when he signed with the company, they simply asked him to take one serving of each product, so they could claim he used them in their advertising. He admitted that aside from this, he never used any of the supplements he endorses.

PATENTS / PATENT-PENDING

As an inventor and patent holder myself, I need to preface this tactic by saying that I have a lot of respect for patents. Many supplement products are under patent, and often these patents are the result of innovative concepts, and a great deal of hard work and dedication. They often represent real scientific advancement in the field, and an honest effort on the part of the inventor to protect his or her hard work. But that is not always the case. I've been through the process front to back enough times to learn what it is all about, at least in a general sense. More to the point, I've come to understand exactly what the words "patented" and "patent-pending" actually tell us about a product.

Advertisers often state that because a product is patented, it was proven to work by the government. Be aware that this is not true. The U.S. Patent Office does not have a lab where it tests inventions. The patent review process is entirely on paper. The main focus of the patent examiner is to make sure the patent represents a concept that is novel (new), and also unobvious to others in the same field. Many patents have been awarded for products with seemingly good ideas that just do not work. Furthermore, the phrase "patent pending" means only that someone has filed a patent. I know of more than one manufacturer that regularly files patents it knows it will never get, simply to put the patent pending claim in their advertising. Note that the patent process can take years, during which time the company has a legal right to say "patent-pending". Patents are often good things, but they can also be pure marketing.

BONDED COMPOUNDS

Developing new sports nutrition ingredients can be a very difficult process. It involves extensive research to find novel compounds, isolating and experimenting with them, developing them into standardized dosage units, and (if the company is very serious about the innovation) validating their effects in a clinical setting. I've been through this process, and it can tell you that it is very expensive, and can take years. There are, however, less complicated ways to create new ingredients to sell. One very common practice is to take two known supplement compounds and molecularly bond them together. Creatine pyruvate, arginine alpha-ketoglutarate, and citrulline malate are all examples of supplements were two ingredients were bonded into one molecule to create a new substance.

A company creating such an ingredient has something completely new to sell. They can market it aggressively, and might even patent it. Consumers need to remember, however, that bonded molecules like these are ultimately digested to their parts. For example, citrulline malate is metabolized in the body to citrulline and malic acid. Creatine pyruvate yields creatine and pyruvic acid. In some cases the new molecule has favorable properties, such as greater bioavailability or a more favorable distribution pattern. In many other cases, however, the new molecule offers no advantage at all. The consumer would receive the same benefit (or lack of) by mixing the two separate ingredients. When you see a new bonded supplement, examine it closely to see what substantiation the manufacturer provides for its use.

DRUG SPIKING

The last marketing tactic I will discuss is perhaps the most troubling. It involves the spiking of natural supplement products with synthetic prescription or designer drugs. There are many natural supplement ingredients worth formulating with. But drugs are drugs. If a manufacturer is willing to spike one of their muscle building products with something such as a synthetic anabolic steroid, it will invariably perform better than its legal counterparts. This may strongly drive sales. The spiking can be discontinued on later runs, the product already selling and making steady money. With little government monitoring, spiking is a practice that can easily go unnoticed. Oddly enough, when it is discovered, the penalties are usually light (often fines and recalls). The dangers in this practice are numerous, and of course, it is arguably unconscionable to allow people to take a drug without their knowledge. Drug spiking is not common, but it does happen.

WHAT TO DO?

If this all seems a little disheartening, try not to lose faith. The field of sports nutrition has been responsible for bringing forth many substantial innovations – many true bodybuilding and performance-enhancing supplements. I have little doubt that there are products available that can help you achieve your personal fitness or athletic goals. So take a deep breath before you walk into the local supplement store for your next purchase. Remind yourself that this is just the business end of a strong scientific field. You are going to encounter many products that are not right for you. You, however, will come across many gems too. Don't rush, take your time, and look at everything closely. Apply the tools that you gain from this book, and you will find the high value/high efficacy products you are looking for.

Protein Primer

Part of being an active athletic individual is making sure enough protein is consumed in the diet. Protein is essential for many things. It provides the raw materials necessary for muscle cell repair and growth. It is an important source of energy for the muscles. It even helps maintain an optimal state of metabolism. Athletes find that diets rich in protein dense foods such as poultry, fish, meat, soy, milk, eggs, cheese, and nuts are the most desirable for gaining muscle mass, increasing strength, and maintaining an optimal level of physical performance. A regular eating schedule (six times per day) consisting of high protein meals is widely recommended. Still, it is often difficult to meet the heightened protein requirements of an athlete with whole foods alone. For this reason, protein supplements have become some of the most popular types of products sold on the sports nutrition market.

COMPLETE VS. INCOMPLETE PROTEINS

Proteins can vary significantly based on their structural makeup. Each protein is made up of individual amino acids, which are linked together in chains called polypeptides. The body breaks down protein into its individual amino acids upon digestion, and assembles them into new proteins as needed. There are 20 different standard amino acids. Of these, 9 are considered "essential" because the body cannot synthesize them. The only source for them is food. All of the essential amino acids must be present in order for the body to be able to synthesize new proteins. We, therefore, view those protein sources that contain all of the essential amino acids as "complete" proteins. These are most desired. Incomplete protein sources can be combined with each other to form complete proteins, provided that the combination includes all of the essential amino acids.

Essential Amino Acids
Histidine
Isoleucine
Leucine
Valine
Lysine
Methionine
Phenylalanine
Threonine
Tryptophan

Non-Essential Amino Acids
Alanine
Arginine
Asparagine
Aspartic Acid
Cysteine
Glutamic acid
Glutamine
Glycine
Proline
Serine
Tyrosine

BRANCHED-CHAIN AMINO ACIDS

Three amino acids — leucine, isoleucine, and valine — are classified separately from the other essential amino acids. These are structurally distinct branched-chain amino acids (BCAA). Branched-chain amino acids are unique for more than just their composition. These amino acids are highly prominent in muscle tissue, and account for 14-18% of its amino acid makeup. As such, these amino acids are integral to muscle protein synthesis. Branched-chain amino acids are also metabolized differently than other amino acids, and can be oxidized in the muscles during exercise for energy. Adequate BCAA levels can increase carbohydrate availability, and help protect the muscles from exercise-induced protein breakdown. Ensuring your diet includes an adequate supply of branched-chain amino acids may help support optimal muscle size, strength, and performance. The use of branched-chain amino acid supplements as ergogenic aids will be discussed in more detail later in this book.

HOW MUCH PROTEIN?

The amount of protein you should consume each day depends on your individual level of activity, and resulting nutritive needs. The U.S. Recommended Dietary Allowance (RDA) for protein is .8 grams per kg of bodyweight per day. This equates to about 60 grams of protein per day for an individual weighing 165 lbs. This level is likely not sufficient for an athletically active person. Studies with strength athletes have shown that a daily requirement of up to 1.8 grams per kg is necessary in order to maintain a positive nitrogen balance, more than double the sedentary figure.[1]   Other studies suggest up to 2 grams per kg per day as being optimal for those undergoing intense weight training.[2] Higher amounts (up to 2.62 grams per kg per day) used in some studies, however, have failed to show a significant additive benefit, and are not recommended.[3] Note that drug using bodybuilders may be capable of utilizing more protein. In healthy athletes, protein diets as high as 2.8 g/kg (grams per kilogram of body weight) per day do not appear to impair kidney function.[4]

Recommended daily protein intake levels based on activity.

Activity	_g/kg per day_ *
Sedentary (not exercising)	.8
Moderate endurance exercise (jogging, cycling)	1.2 – 1.4
Power/Speed athletes (track & field)	1.3 – 1.6
Endurance athletes (marathon, triathlon)	1.5 – 2.0
Martial Arts/Boxing	1.5 – 2.0
Weightlifting/Bodybuilding	1.5 – 2.0

* To calculate in pounds, divide by 2.2.

PROTEIN SUPPLEMENTS

Protein supplements are made from a variety of different sources. The most common of these are egg, milk, and soy. The processing of these raw foods to make a refined powder can be done many different ways, resulting in the removal of different components, and varying nutritive makeup. The balance of essential and nonessential amino acids often varies significantly between products. This may lead some proteins to be more completely utilized for tissue growth and repair than others. There are several different methods for determining the relative quality of each protein source, which will be discussed later in this chapter. Different protein sources may also have distinguishing characteristics with regard to taste, water solubility, digestibility, and the content of other nutritive components. I will now discuss the most common types of protein available.

WHEY PROTEIN

Whey is the most popular source of supplemental protein. Whey is a constituent of cow's milk, and accounts for approximately 20% of its protein content. Most whey is produced as a byproduct of cheese manufacturing. Because of this, whey is extremely abundant in supply. It is also a very low cost high quality source of protein. Whey has an excellent nutrient makeup, including all of the essential amino acids. It is especially high in the branched-chain amino acids, key for muscle protein synthesis. Additionally, whey has more sulfur containing amino acids (cysteine, methionine) than casein. These traits support its slightly higher level of biological utilization compared to the other protein sources detailed in this review.

Whey proteins are found in a number of distinct protein "fractions." The seven most abundant of these fractions are beta-lactoglobulin, alpha-lactalbumin, glycomacropeptides, immunoglobulins, bovine serum albumin (BSA), lactoperoxidase, and lactoferrin. Ad-

vances in manufacturing technologies have allowed for the separation of many individual protein fractions. Studies of their effects have produced evidence that some of these protein fractions may have unique biological and health-supporting activity. The potential benefits of whey protein fractions in humans appear to include anabolic, antiviral, immune system support, anticarcinogenic, and anti-inflammatory activity. The research into the various fractions of whey and their benefits is ingoing.

Whey is considered a "fast" protein source. It is digested very quickly, causing a rapid increase in serum amino acid levels. Clinical studies with tracer-labeled whey protein have demonstrated that blood amino acid levels peak approximately 60-90 minutes after ingestion.[5] This peak is short-lived, however, and not effectively sustained past two to three hours. Because the protein floods the body with amino acids so quickly, some of the protein may be oxidized (wasted) as excess. Whey was shown not to reduce total protein breakdown likely because the increase in amino acid availability is only transient. Because this protein source is so fast digesting, it is an excellent protein to use for replenishing the amino acid pool immediately after training.

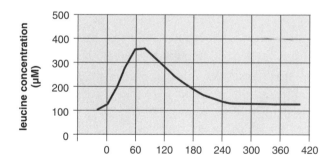

The absorption of amino acids from whey protein over time
(in minutes)

Whey Protein Concentrate (WPC)

Whey protein concentrate (WPC) is the least processed of all the whey protein forms. Because of this, less of the pure protein is separated out. WPC supplements typically contain 70-85% protein by weight. Lower grades containing as little as 30% are also sold, but not widely for consumer use. The remaining calories from WPC come from fat and carbohydrates, particularly lactose, which usually accounts for 4-6% of the weight. Note that some people lack the enzyme necessary to digest lactose, and notice strong gastrointestinal distress when consuming WPC. Whey protein concentrate is the most cost effective form of whey protein. Although some may prefer whey without the fat and sugar, WPC remains an extremely rich source of high quality protein. Whey protein concentrate is thick, and has a fairly distinct taste that can be somewhat difficult to flavor.

Whey Protein Isolate (WPI)

Whey protein also comes in the form of a more purified isolate. Whey protein isolate (WPI) may be produced through ion exchange or membrane filtration technologies, which produce a powder that is at least 90% protein by weight. Whey isolates have much less fat and lactose than concentrates, typically accounting for only 1% of the content. The protein separation technologies used to produce whey isolate usually retain high levels of key protein fractions. Whey isolates are considerably more expensive than concentrates. In addition to the higher protein content, isolates typically have a less noticeable taste than concentrates, and work better as a base for flavoring.

Whey Protein Hydrolysate (WPH)

Whey protein hydrolysate (WPH) is an isolated whey protein that has been partially predigested (hy-

drolyzed). With some of the amino acid peptide bonds broken apart, the protein will contain smaller (more easily digested) peptides. This makes WPH even faster to digest than standard whey concentrates and isolates. The nutrient content of whey hydrolysate is almost identical to standard isolate. It contains about 90% protein by weight, and less than 1% of its content is fat and lactose. Due to the hydrolysis, the BCAA content is slightly lower. WPH is generally more expensive than WPI because of the additional processing. It also tastes bitter compared to other whey proteins, and is usually only added to proteins in small amounts because of this property.

CASEIN PROTEIN

Casein is the most abundant form of protein in cow's milk, accounting for 80% of its protein content. Milk caseins exist in fractions called micelles. These are small spheres of assembled protein chains approximately 100-300 microns in size. The four predominant protein micelles in casein are Beta-CN, AlphaS1-CN, AlphaS2-CN, and Kappa-CN. As with whey protein, there is ongoing study as to the potential unique health benefits to supplementing these protein fractions. Note that some forms of processing to isolate casein proteins can break these micelles. All forms of casein contain a high quality blend of essential, non-essential, and branched chain amino acids. Casein contains a lower percentage of branched-chain amino acids than whey protein, however, and has a lower biological utilization rate.

Casein is identified as a slow digesting protein source. Clinical studies have demonstrated that the appearance of amino acids is slow, steady, and well maintained after ingestion of undenatured (micellar) casein. It produces a stable elevation of amino acids that lasts for up to seven hours. Because there is not a sharp amino acid spike like there is with whey, less protein is generally oxidized. The same investigations also noted that casein increased protein synthesis to a lesser extent than whey, but reduced whole body protein breakdown far more strongly (whey was without effect). Casein produces a greater positive overall protein balance in comparison. Casein is generally regarded as an "anti-catabolic" protein due to its slow acting protein sparing properties. Casein is an ideal

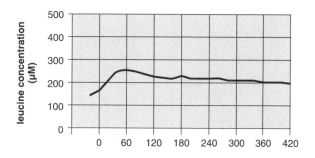

The absorption of amino acids from micellar casein protein (in minutes)

protein for nighttime use, or when meals will be unavailable for more than three hours. Due to its slow digestion, casein is not an ideal post-workout protein source.

Micellar Casein

Micellar casein is an undenatured form of isolated casein protein. Here, the delicate protein micelles are retained by use of a non-chemical filtration process. High in glycomacropeptides and casomorphins, this form of casein has the largest percentage of active protein fractions. It is typically 85-92% protein by weight, with very low levels of fat and lactose. Micellar casein forms a slow digesting clot in the stomach, extending its period of utilization for up to seven hours. Micellar casein is the most expensive form of casein protein available. It also mixes poorly, and has a strong malt taste. As a result, it is often used as a minor part of a protein blend instead of a primary protein source. Micellar casein protein should account

for at least 50% of a protein powder if its slow-digestion properties are desired.

Calcium Caseinate

Calcium caseinate is an isolated form of casein protein. The process used to manufacture this protein breaks down the micelles, forming the protein into a calcium salt. The high quality nutritional value of casein protein is retained. Calcium caseinate has not been studied alongside undenatured (micellar) casein to see if it extends the release of amino acids for as many hours. Calcium caseinate is typically 90% protein by weight, with very low levels of fat (1%) and lactose (.1%). Calcium caseinate is significantly less expensive in comparison to micellar casein. It mixes very well, has good emulsifying properties, and has a less distinct (more neutral) taste.

Potassium Caseinate

This protein is a processed salt of caseinate, similar to calcium caseinate but with a potassium attachment. Potassium caseinate has an almost identical nutrient makeup to calcium caseinate. This salt tends to thicken solutions to a greater extent, however, and is less desirable as a major protein source.

Sodium Caseinate

This protein is a processed salt of caseinate, similar to calcium caseinate but with a sodium attachment. Sodium caseinate has an almost identical nutrient makeup to calcium caseinate. This salt tends to thicken solutions to a greater extent, however, and is less desirable as a major protein source.

MILK PROTEIN

Milk proteins are prepared from skim milk, and contain both whey and casein protein fractions. Milk protein is a rich source of essential and non-essential amino acids, and is well utilized by the body. Milk proteins come in the form of concentrates (MPC) and isolates (MPI) depending on the filtration process and percentage of raw protein yield. Milk protein concentrates range from about 40-85% protein by weight. An 82% milk protein concentrate contains about 4% lactose. All lower yield milk proteins contain significant amounts of lactose (up to 50%). Milk protein isolates contain 90% protein by weight, and only 1% lactose. The separation of milk protein usually involves non-chemical filtration, heating (evaporating), and drying. Some of the delicate protein micelles are retained in both MPC and MPI proteins.

EGG PROTEIN

Egg protein comes in various powdered forms for use in protein shakes. The powder is typically isolated from the white of the egg. Egg is a rich source of complete protein. It has the benefit of being low in fat, and contains no lactose. Although egg has all of the essential amino acids, the overall content of these key amino acids is lower than milk proteins. Egg does contain the branched-chain amino acids, though they are not ideally balanced. It is not regarded as a strong BCAA source for this reason. Because of these factors, the body does not utilize the amino acids from egg whites as completely as it does the milk proteins. Still, powdered egg protein remains an excellent source of supplemental protein for athletic individuals.

SOY PROTEIN ISOLATE

Soybean is a rich vegetable source of complete protein. Soy protein powder is typically refined from soy flour that has had its fat content removed. Soy protein is high in essential and non-essential amino acids, though the balance of essential amino acids is less ideal for human utilization than the milk proteins. Soy

protein does have a significantly higher content of glutamine than whey, however, which is also an abundant amino acid in skeletal muscle and believed important for muscle protein anabolism. Soy protein isolate (SPI) powders typically contain 90% protein by weight, and have very little fat or carbohydrates. Soy is also rich in isoflavones, which have varying biological properties. Some are weak plant-based estrogens (phytoestrogens). Soy isolate is typically the preferred supplemental source of protein for vegetarians.

WHEAT GLUTEN

Wheat gluten is a low quality source of protein made from the grains of wheat. It does not contain all of the essential amino acids, and is, therefore, an incomplete protein. This protein source is particularly low in both lysine and threonine. Gluten should, therefore, be combined with other proteins rich in these essential amino acids in order for the body to properly utilize it. For athletic individuals, gluten is considered an inferior protein source compared to other commercially available proteins. Sport supplement manufacturers mainly use it for its low cost aspect, as it can bulk out the volume of more expensive whey- or casein-based protein powders, reducing production costs.

RATING PROTEIN QUALITY

Protein quality refers to the ability of the body to utilize a protein for necessary functions, and minimize amino acid oxidation and waste. No protein source is utilized 100%. Furthermore, not all proteins are equal in their rate of utilization. Much of this is due to the profile of amino acids that is unique to each. The body typically does not utilize about 30% of the content of a high quality protein. The loss in utilization can be as high as 60% with a low quality protein source. A variety of scientific methods have been developed for determining the relative quality of a protein. This section discusses some of the most popular and widely referenced methods, with an emphasis on the ratings for each of our reviewed sources.

Protein Efficiency Ratio (PER)

Protein Efficiency Ratio is one of the longest and most widely used protein rating methods. PER is determined by measuring the growth of laboratory rats over time when fed from a particular source. It is a calculation based on the weight gain in relation to the weight of protein consumed. A protein source with a PER above 2.5 is generally considered a high quality source of protein. The maximum value according to

Protein	PER
Beef	2.9
Casein	2.5
Egg	3.9
Milk	2.5
Soy Protein	2.2
Wheat Gluten	0.8
Whey Protein	3.2

the PER scale is about 4.4. PER is considered a reliable method for determining general protein quality, even if it does not directly pertain to the nutritive needs of athletes. It has, however, been criticized for under-representing the quality of plant-based proteins such as soy isolate.

Biological Value (BV)

Biological value measures the quality of a protein by looking at its retention in an animal (rat). BV is calculated by measuring the amount of nitrogen used for tissue formation (protein synthesis), and dividing it

by the nitrogen absorbed from the diet (it is a measure of absorbed nitrogen retained).[7] The nitrogen atom is found in protein, but not carbohydrates or fats. This makes it an excellent basis for determining the disposition of dietary protein. Full retention of nitrogen (none excreted in the urine) indicates that the

Protein	BV
Beef	80
Casein	77
Egg	100
Milk	91
Soy Protein	74
Wheat Gluten	64
Whey Protein	104

organism utilized all of a given protein. This results in a BV score of 100 (BV is expressed as a percent of utilization). Whole egg was used as the basis for the biological value test because, at the time it was developed, egg was thought to be the most utilizable protein source.

Net Protein Utilization (NPU)

The net protein utilization method for determining protein quality is very similar to the biological value test. The main difference between the two is that BV is based on protein absorbed, while NPU is based on total protein ingested (it is a measure of ingested protein retained). NPU can be determined by using nitrogen balance testing, although it can also involve sacrificing the animal for more accurate measurements. NPU is reflected in percentage utilized. A value of 100 indicates 100% utilization of the nitro-

Protein	NPU
Beef	80
Casein	70
Egg	94
Milk	82
Soy Protein	61
Wheat Gluten	23
Whey Protein	92

gen (protein synthesis). A value of 0 indicates that none of the nitrogen supplied was utilized for protein synthesis. NPU testing is often criticized for being subject to high levels of variation as the amount of protein consumed in studies deviates from the recommended daily intake.[8]

Protein Digestibility Corrected Amino Acid Score (PDCAAS)

The protein digestibility corrected amino acid score measures the quality of a protein based on its profile

Protein	PDCAAS
Beef	0.92
Casein	1.00
Egg	1.00
Milk	1.00
Soy Protein	1.00
Wheat Gluten	0.25
Whey Protein	1.00

of essential and non-essential amino acids. It is specifically calculated by looking at the ratio between the first limiting essential amino acid in the protein, and the amino acid requirement of a child 2-5 years. The PDCAAS is presently the most widely used method for evaluating the quality of a protein source. It is the standard methodology used by the World Health Organization, and widely regarded by medical professionals as the most relevant for human use. Note that the PDCAAS method does not take into account what other factors can have on protein utilization, such as protein digestibility, the influence of other nutritive components, and the value of proteins with higher levels of essential amino acids.

CHOOSING THE RIGHT PROTEIN

In my opinion, it is a mistake to get too caught up thinking about protein sources. Supplement manufacturers love to market complicated high cost proteins, especially multi-source blends. This is done for market differentiation and margin expansion, as there is very little profit to be made selling standard commodity proteins unless you are an enormous producer. Realistically, there is not much functional need to change the amino acid profile of such high quality protein sources as whey and casein. Provided you can digest lactose, a whey concentrate can provide an excellent source for fast amino acids for after training and short gaps between meals. A high quality whey isolate should have low enough lactose for sensitive individuals. Micellar casein is also recommended for its slow digesting properties, especially for use at bedtime and when there are long gaps between meals. For those that cannot tolerate milk products, egg protein powder should be preferred. Remember too, protein powders are meant to supplement whole foods rich in protein, not replace them.

Carbohydrate Supplementation

Of the three classes of nutrients (fats, proteins, and carbohydrates), carbohydrates are the most active source of fuel during exercise. Carbohydrates in their most basic form are simple sugar molecules called monosaccharides. The most common monosaccharides are glucose, galactose, and fructose. Larger carbohydrates are made up of two or more monosaccharides in a chain, referred to as disaccharides, trisaccharides, or polysaccharides depending on the number of sugars. Carbohydrates are broadly categorized as either simple or complex, depending on the length of these sugar chains. The body must digest carbohydrates down to their monosaccharide forms before they can be absorbed and utilized for energy.

Glucose is the primary monosaccharide fuel source in human metabolism. While blood glucose can be utilized immediately for energy, it may also be converted to glycogen for later use. Glycogen, which is stored mainly in the muscles and liver, represents the body's principle energy reservoir during anaerobic exercise. It is also important to performance in endurance (aerobic) activities. The level of stored glycogen will vary depending on size, training status, and diet. We humans typically store about 300-400 grams of glycogen in our muscles, and another 80-100 grams in the liver.[9] This may be considerably higher in athletic individuals with significant muscle mass and training. Glycogen stores are usually sufficient to provide energy for 90-180 minutes of exercise at moderate intensity.[10] High intensity exercise may deplete glycogen stores within 30 minutes. Once these glycogen stores are depleted, a significant decrease in performance will result, as the body will be forced to rely upon less efficient sources of fuel.[11]

THE GLYCEMIC INDEX

The glycemic index is a system of categorizing foods based on the impact they have on blood sugar levels. It was developed to help diabetic patients better control their blood sugar levels through diet. The main factor dictating where a food fits in this index is its rate of digestion. Slower digesting foods and carbohydrate sources tend to produce lower peaks in blood sugar, and are considered less "glycemic." The glycemic index gives each food a glycemic rating depending on its propensity to increase blood sugar. This GI rating generally ranges from 0 (no blood sugar response) to 100 (maximum increase), although certain rapid-digesting carbohydrates are listed above 100 on some glycemic index scales. Foods with a GI rating of 55 or below are considered low GI. A GI of 56-69 is considered moderate, and 77 or above high.

By extension of their less dramatic effects on blood sugar levels, foods with a lower glycemic rating tend to produce lower levels of peak insulin secretion. This has implications beyond just the management of diabetes. For example, high GI foods tend to increase the likelihood of body fat retention, as insulin is involved in nutrient (fat) storage.[12] Those wishing to reduce body weight usually find dieting more successful when low or moderate GI foods are consumed instead of sugars. Excess blood sugar and insulin elevations can also have deleterious effects on health. Diets high in simple sugars are not advised, and are associated with various diseases including metabolic syndrome, diabetes, cancer, and heart disease.[13, 14] There are many instances, however, when athletes may also find advantages to using high glycemic carbohydrate sources.

GLYCEMIC INDEX VALUES OF COMMON CARBOHYDRATE SOURCES

Fructose	32[15]	Maltose	150
Lactose	65	Trehalose	67[16]
Honey	83	Maltitol	36[17]
High fructose corn syrup	89	Xylitol	13
Sucrose	92	Isomalt	9
Glucose	137	Sorbitol	9
Maltodextrin	137	Lactitol	6
White sugar	142		

CARBOHYDRATE SUPPLEMENTATION BEFORE EXERCISE

Carbohydrate supplementation before exercise may help preserve muscle glycogen stores and extend muscle endurance. Supplementation will have its greatest impact if muscle glycogen stores are low at the start of exercise, and may not even be necessary if the exercise duration is short. Effective carbohydrate sources for pre-workout supplementation may include either high GI or low GI carbohydrates, as both seem to support training equally provided that blood glucose is maintained. Drinks containing simple carbohydrates are most common, and no individual sugar is considered to be more advantageous over others. For example, one study found similar levels of performance during a 10 km run when subjects consumed a drink containing fructose, glucose, or a sugar/glucose blend before the event.[18] While recommendations often vary, the consumption of 30-60 grams of a simple carbohydrate blend 30-60 minutes before exercise is usually sufficient.

CARBOHYDRATE SUPPLEMENTATION DURING EXERCISE

The supplementation of carbohydrates before exercise may not be sufficient to sustain blood glucose concentrations throughout the full period of activity. It may be necessary to supplement carbohydrates during exercise, especially if the intensity is high, or the duration is going to exceed one hour. The importance of such a supplement may also increase if no pre-workout carbohydrate drink has been consumed. Given the need for rapid replenishment, the carbohydrate drink to use during exercise should contain a moderate dose of easily digested high GI carbohydrates such as glucose (dextrose), sugar, and maltodextrin.

Glucose appears to be effectively absorbed through the small intestine at a rate of about one gram per minute.[19,20] Intakes above this level may cause gastrointestinal distress, which can interfere with performance. It is generally advised to drink 7.5-15 grams of simple carbohydrates every 15 minutes during exercise, or a total of 30-60 grams slowly each hour. Studies also show that the addition of protein, essential amino acids, or branched-chain amino acids can reduce protein catabolism compared to the use of carbohydrates alone. For this purpose, the use of 6-15 grams of protein per hour may be adequate.

CARBOHYDRATE SUPPLEMENTATION AFTER EXERCISE

The window immediately after exercise is considered the most crucial for nutrient uptake and recovery/growth. The resynthesis potential of glycogen is at its maximum during the first 30-60 minutes after exercise, and is significantly elevated for two hours.[21] During this time, the supplementation of high GI carbohydrate sources is advised to maximize glycogen retention. Studies show that glycogen levels can be replenished to near baseline levels within 24 hours when the post-exercise recovery window includes optimal carbohydrate consumption.[22] They also show that if sufficient carbohydrates are not supplied within two hours of training, glycogen resynthesis is drastically slowed, and replenishment may take much longer.[23] Maximum glycogen replenishment has been noted when high levels of carbohydrates (1-1.85 g/kg/hour) are given every hour for five hours post training.[24,25]

Insulin sensitivity, amino acid transport, and protein synthesis potential in the muscles are also intensified during the post-exercise recovery period.[26,27,28] Studies show that a combination of protein and carbohydrates during this period maximizes protein synthesis rates and the retention of glycogen, and minimizes protein catabolism.[29,30] The exact needs of the athlete will be dependent on the type of activity, the training status, individual metabolic factors, and the level of exercise intensity. Those undergoing low to moderate intensity exercise may find the consumption of 30 grams of carbohydrates and 10-20 grams of protein during the first two hours after exercise to be ade-

quate. For those in high intensity training or bodybuilding programs, a minimum intake of 100 grams of carbohydrates and 25-50 grams of protein during the first two hours after exercise is usually recommended.

CARBOHYDRATE LOADING (PRIOR TO ENDURANCE COMPETITION)

Total body carbohydrate storage can be maximized (beyond normal levels) during a process of carbohydrate loading. This is a common practice for endurance athletes, and typically involves the consumption of very high levels of carbohydrates for up to one week prior to an endurance competition. They may also employ a period of carbohydrate restriction and depletion for five to seven days prior to the loading phase. There is, however, no solid evidence that the practice of pre-depletion is beneficial.[31] For peak glycogen loading it is recommended to consume 600-1,000 grams of carbohydrates per day for six days prior to competition.[32]

"EXOTIC" CARBOHYDRATES

In addition to the basic carbohydrate sources commonly used for the manufacture of glycogen support supplements such as glucose (dextrose), fructose, sugar (sucrose), and maltodextrin, some sport supplement companies heavily market the use of more exotic carbohydrate sources. These carbohydrates may have varying properties with regard to sweetness, rate of digestion, and glycemic effect. With regard to sports nutrition, however, the purpose of all carbohydrate supplements is to provide usable sugar for energy metabolism. It is questionable whether these exotic carbohydrates offer tangible ergogenic benefits compared to the use of basic carbohydrates.

SUGAR ALCOHOLS

Sugar alcohols are a unique family of carbohydrates that have combined sugar and alcohol components. Some sugar alcohols are found in certain plant species. Many others are synthetic derivatives of sugars. Many sugar alcohols are only partially absorbed, and therefore provide fewer calories per gram, and have a lower glycemic effect than sugar.[33] Many also have reduced sweetness properties, however, and more may have to be consumed when attempting to replace natural sugar. Some sugar alcohols also have unique properties. For example, bacteria in the mouth does not readily consume xylitol. It is not associated with tooth decay, and makes a promising sweetener for use in chewing gums.[34] It is unlikely that sugar alcohols offer any ergogenic advantage over the consumption of regular carbohydrates.

Trehalose is a disaccharide consisting of two glucose molecules connected by an alpha-1,1-glycosidic bond.[35] This carbohydrate is unique in that it cannot be broken down in the mouth, and it only metabolizes to glucose by intestinal bacteria. Trehalose has a lower glycemic effect than most basic sugars (GI 67), and is promoted in sports nutrition as a slow digesting alternative for better glycogen replenishment. Studies do not support this claim, however, and suggest that trehalose may actually be inferior to glucose for supporting exercise performance.[36] It is presently unknown if trehalose offers any ergogenic advantage compared to the consumption of regular carbohydrates.

Waxy Maize Starch is a high molecular weight starch extracted from certain plants such as corn and rice. It is especially high in amylopectin, a highly branched polymer of glucose. Waxy maize starch is sometimes promoted as a rapid source of glucose for the muscles, enabling a higher level of glycogen resynthesis. Studies, however, show this starch is actually slower to digest and peak (glucose) in the blood than high GI carbohydrates such as a maltodextrin and sugar.[37] Waxy maize starch may offer some value as a steady carbohydrate source, but does not appear at this time to have any special properties with regard to glycogen replenishment after exercise.[38] It also does not appear that waxy maize starch has an ergogenic advantage compared to the consumption of regular carbohydrates.[39]

Vitargo is the brand name for a patented high molecular weight starch fraction that is obtained from certain plants. Although it is derived from waxy maize starch, it is considerably different from this carbohydrate source. Vitargo appears to have the benefit of fast gastric emptying, which means that it leaves the stomach and enters the small intestine (where it can be absorbed) much faster than glucose or other common sugars.[40] Studies have also shown that Vitargo causes a much higher retention of glycogen (+68%) two hours after exercise compared to the use of maltodextrin and dextrose.[41] After four hours, however, there are no significant differences between carbohydrate sources. Vitargo appears to be a promising carbohydrate for supplementation, especially when the rapid replenishment of glycogen after exercise is required.[42] It is, however, unknown if the regular use of Vitargo offers any ergogenic advantage compared to the consumption of common replenishment carbohydrates such as dextrose, sugar, fructose, or maltodextrin.

Vitamins and Minerals

While the focus of this book is the review of ergogenic supplements, it is important to discuss, at least briefly, some general aspects of nutrition. We have already discussed the protein and carbohydrate requirements of athletes, and the various forms of supplementation. This section pertains to vitamins and minerals. These organic and inorganic components of the diet (respectively) are also considered essential, as they are not produced (or not sufficiently produced) in the body, and are necessary for many of the body's functions. This includes such basic activities as the utilization of nutrients, the maintenance of metabolism, and the transport of oxygen. While we will not discuss the full physiological role of each vitamin, nor detail all minerals and elements, in this section, we will go over those with activities that may be tied with physical performance.

It is important to emphasize that vitamins and minerals are generally not considered ergogenic substances. If you are meeting all of your daily needs, a vitamin/mineral supplement is unlikely to improve your exercise performance.[43] Many vitamin or mineral deficiencies, however, are likely to hinder your ability to maintain optimal energy output during, or recovery from, training. In many cases, it may be an unrecognized deficit in the dietary intake of a key vitamin or mineral that could be responsible for stagnated performance. This is important, as a person could be searching for a strong ergogenic supplement to trigger progress, and the very thing they need is a basic vitamin and mineral supplement. Evaluating your diet, activity, and supplementation to avoid deficiencies is, therefore, strongly recommended as a starting point of any supplementation program.

For the sake of reference, vitamin and mineral listings have been added that include the current recommended dietary allowances (according to the U.S. Department of Agriculture) for men aged 31-50 years. An asterisk (*) denotes that the FDA considers this amount adequate, but no official recommended dietary allowance (RDA) has been established. These recommended vitamin and mineral intake amounts may vary considerably for women, pregnant women, or men of different ages. Intense exercise may also increase the metabolic requirements for some vitamins and minerals, although a complete understanding of the heightened needs of athletes at different levels of training is lacking. For this reason, it is often advised to consume a low dose vitamin and mineral supplement just to be sure, especially during periods of high intensity exercise.

VITAMIN ALLOWANCES (MEN 31-50)

Vitamin A (900 mcg)

Vitamin C (90 mg)

Vitamin D (5 mcg*)

Vitamin E (15 mg)

Vitamin K (120 mcg*)

Thiamin (1.2 mg)

Riboflavin (1.3 mg)

Niacin (16 mg)

Vitamin B6 (1.3 mg)

Folate (400 mcg)

Vitamin B12 (2.4 mg)

Pantothenic Acid (5 mg*)

Biotin (30 mcg*)

Choline (550 mg*)

Choline is a relative of the B family of vitamins. Choline is important to the stability and functioning of cell membranes, as well as cell signaling. It is also involved in the metabolism of fats, and supports the synthesis of acetylcholine, a principle neurotransmitter.

Vitamin A (retinol) is involved in the growth and development of cells, and the support of vision and immunity. It also has some antioxidant capacity. Optimal levels may help reduce oxidative stress during exercise.

Vitamin B1 (thiamin) is involved in the metabolism of glucose for energy. It is key to cell functioning in many tissues, including the nervous system, heart, and muscles. Optimal levels may help prevent exercise fatigue.

Vitamin B2 (riboflavin) is involved in the metabolism of carbohydrates for energy and red blood cell production. Riboflavin requirements may significantly increase with exercise.[44] A deficiency in riboflavin may reduce aerobic exercise performance.[45]

Vitamin B3 (niacin) is involved in the production of cellular energy from food. It is very active in muscle cells, and necessary for muscle function. While a niacin deficiency may hinder performance, excess levels are also believed to diminish exercise capacity.

Vitamin B5 (pantothenic acid) is involved in the metabolism of fats, carbohydrates, and proteins. It also plays a role in neurotransmitter synthesis. Pantothenic acid is important to muscle energy production,[46] and optimal levels may improve oxygen consumption and reduce lactic acid buildup during exercise.[47]

Vitamin B6 (pyridoxine) is involved in the metabolism of proteins, and the production of oxygen carrying red blood cells.

Vitamin B7 (biotin) is involved in the metabolism of fatty acids and amino acids. This vitamin is also commonly known as Vitamin H.

Vitamin B9 (folic acid) is necessary for the production of cellular DNA, as well as oxygen carrying red blood cells.

Vitamin B12 (cobalamin) is important to nervous system functioning, as well as the production of oxygen carrying red blood cells.

Vitamin C (ascorbic acid) is involved in a wide variety of biological functions, including energy metabolism, collagen formation, bone retention, and vascular stability. It is also the body's principle water-soluble antioxidant, and may help remove free radicals from cells (which may hinder performance).

Vitamin D (calcitriol) influences more than 1,000 responsive genes in the body, and has activities in a variety of tissues including the bone, nervous system, and muscle. Vitamin D is produced when you are exposed to the sun, and is also found in some foods. Some studies suggest that performance is optimal when blood levels are higher.[48]

Vitamin E (tocopherols) is important to oxygen carrying red blood cells. It is also the body's principle fat-soluble antioxidant, and has been shown to help reduce markers of oxidative stress during exercise.[49]

Vitamin K (phylloquinone) is important to cell growth, bone health, and hematological function. Deficiencies in vitamin K are rare.

Mineral and Element Allowances (men 31-50)

Calcium (1,000 mg*)

Chromium (35 mcg*)

Copper (900 mcg)

Fluoride (4 mg*)

Iodine (150 mcg)

Iron (8 mg)

Magnesium (420 mg)

Manganese (2.3 mg*)

Molybdenum (45 mcg*)

Phosphorus (700 mg)

Selenium (55 mcg)

Zinc (11 mg)

Potassium (4.7 mg*)

Sodium (1,500 mg*)

Chloride (2.3 mg*)

Calcium is widely known to be a basic component of the bones. It is also integrally involved in cell biology, and helps control a wide variety of activities including muscle contractions. Studies also suggest that calcium can help increase the level of free testosterone in exercising athletes.[50]

Chromium is involved in supporting insulin sensitivity in skeletal muscle tissue. This may allow it to facilitate the metabolism of glucose, as well as muscle glycogen storage.

Iron is key to the function of red blood cells, and the delivery of oxygen to body tissues. Iron deficiency is sometimes associated with anemia, or clinically reduced red blood cell concentrations. Iron is highly oxidative, and dietary iron deficiency is rare in men. Iron supplementation is usually not needed for this group unless a specific deficiency has been identified.

Magnesium is involved in cell physiology, including glucose metabolism and oxygen transport. It is important to the functioning of many tissues, including the bones, central nervous system, and muscles. Like calcium, it is integral to muscle contraction.

Phosphorous is another key component of cell physiology, and is involved in a diverse set of activities including the support of membrane stability, metabolism, and DNA synthesis. It also serves as a key component in both aerobic and anaerobic energy production. Studies suggest that phosphate loading (sodium phosphate, 4 g/day for 6 days) can increase endurance exercise performance.[51]

Potassium is important in the regulation of the body's water balance. It is also involved in glucose metabolism, and is key to the functioning of many cells including the heart and muscles. Excess potassium can be dangerous, and supplementation beyond a normal multivitamin should not be attempted without medical need.

Selenium supports the production of certain antioxidant enzymes, and may help reduce free radical damage to cells (which may be increased during exercise). It is also important to the functioning of the thyroid.

Zinc is involved in testosterone synthesis and immunity. While zinc deficiency is rare, it may lead to impaired testosterone production and increased susceptibility to infection. Excess zinc can also suppress HDL (good) cholesterol, and interfere with copper absorption.[52]

Studs and Duds – The Rating System

Each sport supplement ingredient reviewed in this book has been evaluated for efficacy in two parts. The first examination is at the clinical level. This concerns any scientific data or actual human trials that can help us determine the value of said ingredient as a performance-enhancing supplement. The second evaluation is of empirical evidence. This is an informal assessment of common observations with the use of the ingredient as a standalone item. In both cases, attempts have been made to obtain the most reliable and relevant data available. A traditional rating system of 1 to 5 represents the strength of each evaluation, and the combined score is used for the overall rating.

CLINICAL EVIDENCE

The clinical study of a sport supplement ingredient can take on many different forms. Sometimes it is as simple as a test tube experiment, where the investigators are looking for a particular hormone or chemical to be produced when cells are incubated with the supplement. At other times, they can be as complicated as a full university investigation, where the supplement or a placebo is given to human volunteers and a detailed accounting of all results is noted. Generally, the more detailed and extensive a study is, the more valuable are its conclusions. A positive response in a double blind placebo controlled study on individuals with consistent exercise or athletic experience is

CLINICAL STUDIES SCORECARD

Score	
5	The ingredient has been shown to improve body composition or performance in a placebo-controlled study of experienced athletes or resistance-trained individuals.
4	The ingredient has been shown to improve body composition or performance in a placebo-controlled study of untrained (sedentary) individuals.
3	The ingredient has been shown in placebo-controlled human studies to improve a metabolic marker (e.g., testosterone, IGF-1 levels) often linked to positive changes in body composition or performance.
2	The ingredient has been shown to improve body composition, performance, or a metabolic marker associated with potential improvements in experiments on laboratory animals.
1	There is in-vitro ("test tube") evidence that the ingredient might be able to improve body composition, performance, or a related metabolic marker in humans.

Note that only studies published in reputable peer reviewed journals have been included in this review.

considered the highest level of clinical validation or "proof" available for a sport supplement.

Understanding Clinical Studies

To understand why validation in a placebo-controlled study is valued so highly, we need to examine just how strict these studies are. To begin with, a reputable study is designed from top to bottom to eliminate all influence of bias. This goes as far as "group randomization," which assures that neither the participants nor the investigators know who is actually taking the supplement and who is taking the placebo until the study is completed ("double blind" study). This eliminates any chance an investigator might subconsciously favor one group over the other. All relevant protocols in the study are also disclosed, so there should be no guessing as to how the study was conducted, and how measurements were taken. Credible studies are also peer reviewed, which means that other researchers in the same field have had the opportunity to critically evaluate its techniques before publication.

Strength in Numbers

Just as important as removing bias in a study, is removing the influence of random chance. After all, if you subject two groups of people to exercise, one will perform better than the other given the influence of individual genetic, dietary, and motivational factors. But you cannot draw a conclusion based solely on which groups did better — you need to be sure one group did better because of the supplement. By using large group sizes and measuring each of the individual responses, a reputable study tries to prove an association between the intervention (the supplement) and the observed effect (the result) mathematically. Generally, the larger and more homogenous (equal in makeup) the groups are, the less influence individual factors will have on the outcome, and the more certain one can be of any association.

Science takes its widest steps forward on a foundation of certainty. While strong associations can tell us a great deal, a "statistically significant" mathematical association is required before any credible study can report something as a positive result. This is usually defined as a 95% probability or greater that the result would be repeated under the same conditions. In other words, based on all the individual and group total responses, we must be 95% sure or better that the supplement was responsible for the improvements. This is a very high threshold. So high, in fact, that for years studies giving anabolic steroids to athletes routinely failed to prove they actually increased muscle mass or performance. Only when the studies became larger, and the protocols better tailored to noticing these improvements, was the medical community able to reconcile the observations of athletes.

Because of these strict standards, we hold clinical validation in extremely high regard. Very few sport supplements have actually achieved this level of efficacy proof, and the ones that have are usually regarded as products of extremely high reliability. Still, it is important that we not focus solely on statistically significant results. Very often the population sizes or protocols of a study are not strong enough to achieve significant figures. We are often left with strong positive associations that are just not quite "provable." An association that is seen with an 80-95% confidence level is usually regarded as a "statistically strong trend" or a "non-significant improvement." Such strong associations help researchers focus their studies in the future. In a field easily influenced by individual factors, we too can learn a great deal from statistically strong trends. As you read this book, please pay close attention to such details under the Clinical Studies section for each supplement.

Body Composition

On this same note, if you are looking for studies proving that a supplement will help you make significant improvements in total muscle mass, know these studies are few and far between. Changes in body composition can be very difficult to control in a clinical setting, as they are easily influenced by many individual and methodological factors. We all know that some people gain muscle mass more easily than others, regardless of supplementation. This makes proving effect across small group populations difficult. Generally, changes in strength and performance numbers are easier to demonstrate. An absence of statistically significant findings on body composition in a study, therefore, does not necessarily represent a lack of effect. With the understanding that underlying changes in body composition are likely to go unnoticed, we typically look for performance improvements during resistance training, and extrapolate how they will relate to body mass over time.

EMPIRICAL EVIDENCE

Clinical studies can be time-consuming to design and implement. They are also very expensive. It can take years before a detailed study is conducted on a popular sport nutrition ingredient, especially one that relates to a relevant group of exercise-experienced individuals. If and when they are conducted, it can often take time, and repeat investigations, to draw out statistically significant findings. The sports nutrition industry, on the other hand, is very fast paced and innovation driven. New supplements come out all the time. Because of this, we cannot rely solely on clinical evidence when trying to determine the value of a sport supplement. We must also examine the real-world responses people have been noticing from the ingredient.

EMPIRICAL EVIDENCE SCORECARD

Score

5   STRONGLY POSITIVE: A strong majority of people taking this supplement in adequate dosages report positive experiences.

4   POSITIVE: A majority (more than half) of people taking this supplement in adequate dosages report positive experiences.

3   MIXED: The experiences with this supplement are very mixed, with many positive and negative experiences reported.

2   NEGATIVE: A minority (less than half) of users seem to have positive results with this supplement. More users fail to notice a substantial effect.

1   HIGHLY NEGATIVE: A strong majority of users fail to notice a positive response from this supplement.

Each supplement reviewed in this book also includes a summary of empirical evidence pertaining to its use. By its nature, empirical evidence, or evidence based solely on observation, is less reliable that substantiated clinical evidence. It is subject to interpretation, and always lends itself to some bias in the part of the interpreter. Also, when people have expectations about the effects of a product, they sometimes notice positive changes that are not actually there ("placebo effect"). Still, in a fast-paced industry such as this, empirical evidence is a fundamental asset provided you are able to rely on the source. In this regard, I have done my best to be objective and critical. Whenever possible, I drew on my own observations, as well as the observations of other researchers in the field whose opinions I value.

Ingredient Profiles

Acetyl-L-Carnitine (ALCAR)

syn. acetyl-levocarnitine
syn. levacecarnine

PERFORMANCE VALIDATION SCORES	
Combined	6
Clinical Support Rating	2
Empirical Evidence Rating	4

Description:

Acetyl-l-carnitine (ALCAR) is a naturally occurring metabolite and precursor of L-carnitine, a key intermediary in fatty acid oxidation and cellular energy metabolism. It is synthesized in various tissues of the body, including the brain, liver, and kidneys.[53] It is also produced in the muscles during high intensity exercise, particularly when performing above the lactate threshold (where serum lactate is increased).[54] Although a metabolite of carnitine, acetyl-l-carnitine also plays an active role in energy metabolism. It is important to the central nervous system, where (among other things) it is involved in the synthesis of the neurotransmitter acetylcholine.[55] ALCAR supplements are widely sold to treat physical and mental fatigue, and improve memory, mood, and cognitive performance.

Acetyl-l-carnitine also possesses some characteristics that might allow its supplementation to increase athletic performance. For example, like L-carnitine, ALCAR is involved in the metabolism of fatty acids for energy.[56] This might help preserve optimal ATP concentrations for prolonged performance. Acetyl-l-carnitine may also attenuate insulin resistance,[57] which could help better partition nutrients into muscle cells, and away from fat storage. Studies also suggest that under certain metabolic conditions, ALCAR might increase protein synthesis rates and prevent protein catabolism.[58,59] To date, however, this supplement has not been shown in human clinical studies to have ergogenic activity.

Promoted Benefits:

Acetyl-l-carnitine is promoted to increase energy, and improve overall sports/exercise performance.

Clinical Studies:

Although acetyl-l-carnitine supplementation has been the subject of extensive clinical study in humans, data on its potential use as a sport supplement is extremely limited. The use of acetyl-l-carnitine as a sport supplement is presently supported by animal data only. Its Clinical Support Rating is 2 (2/5).

The most widely referenced study of acetyl-l-carnitine examined its effects on body composition in young and old male rats.[60] The animals were supplemented with ALCAR in their drinking water for one month, at a concentration of 15 g per liter. The results showed that old animals supplemented with this nutrient gained more lean body mass than control animals, while young supplemented rats gained less body fat in comparison. Older animals consuming ALCAR also tended to have more ATP than unsupplemented control animals.

There have only been a few human studies of potential relevance. One examined the prolonged use of acetyl-l-carnitine in a group of HIV+ men.[61] Subjects consumed three grams of ALCAR daily for five months. Although exercise performance was not measured as part of this study, the researchers did examine the serum level of IGF-1 (Insulin-like Growth Factor-1), an anabolic hormone. The supplementation of acetyl-l-carnitine appeared to significantly increase IGF-1 levels. This study, however, was not placebo-controlled. It may also address the particular metabolic needs of these patients, and not necessarily represent the effects of carnitine in a healthy population.

A second human study examined the effects of acetyl-l-carnitine on chronic fatigue syndrome in a group of elderly patients.[62] ALCAR supplementation produced positive changes in certain aspects of both mental and physical fatigue. Another study compared the benefits of 2 g/daily of either acetyl-l-carnitine or propionyl-l-carnitine on mental and physical fatigue in patients with chronic fatigue syndrome.[63] Both supplementation protocols resulted in marked improvements, though propionyl-l-carnitine produced benefits with regard to physical fatigue, while ALCAR only improved mental fatigue measures. This study was also not placebo-controlled.

Further research is needed to determine if the supplementation of acetyl-l-carnitine has ergogenic value in trained adults.

Empirical Evidence:

Acetyl-l-carnitine is widely available as a stand-alone nutritional supplement. The feedback on its use as a sport supplement tends to be positive. The main point of positive feedback usually involves mental focus and improved nutrient partitioning effects, particularly with regard to the decreased retention of fat. Many bodybuilders comment that ALCAR is effec-tive for helping to maintain a state of lean muscle mass accrual, especially during periods of higher calorie intake (bulking diets). Some users also report improvements in muscle endurance and athletic performance, although this appears to be a less consistent result. A minority of users claim to notice no benefit at all from acetyl-l-carnitine supplementation. Whether this is due to an individual insensitivity to ALCAR, other confounding variables, or a true lack of ergogenic value remains unclear. Acetyl-l-carnitine has an Empirical Evidence Rating of 4 (4/5).

Effective Dosage:

An effective dosage of this supplement has not been established. Manufacturers commonly recommend 1,000-3,000 mg per day.

Side Effects / Safety:

Acetyl-l-carnitine was well tolerated during clinical studies, with no significant side effects.

Adenosine Triphosphate (ATP)

syn. adenosine 5'-triphosphate disodium

PERFORMANCE VALIDATION SCORES	
Combined	8
Clinical Support Rating	5
Empirical Evidence Rating	3

Description:

Adenosine triphosphate (ATP) is the main energy carrier for all living cells. As such, it is necessary for most cellular functions, and key to such basic processes as the synthesis of DNA, RNA, and proteins, and the transport of molecules across cell membranes. It is also necessary for muscle contractions, and is integral to both anaerobic and aerobic energy metabolism. ATP is metabolized to adenosine diphosphate (ADP) and phosphate in order to release energy, which is specifically provided by the hydration of free phosphate. ADP is constantly recycled back into its original ATP form as part of the ATP-dependent energy cycle, though its levels become lowered as a part of fatigue. Adenosine triphosphate (as a disodium salt) is widely available as a sport supplement ingredient.

Although the body produces ample amounts of ATP, its additional supplementation may still be of value. Oral administration has been shown to increase ATP concentrations in tissue and serum.[64] With this it is also capable of producing a number of biological effects. For example, ATP has been shown to increase blood flow to peripheral tissues, which might improve nutrient and oxygen delivery.[65] It has also been shown to reduce lower back pain,[66] and is actually an approved drug product in France (Atepadene, Mayoly-Spindler) for this purpose. ATP supplementation by healthy adults may be useful for improving energy and muscle endurance during exercise as well, although further research is needed to independently validate this.

Promoted Benefits:

Adenosine triphosphate is promoted to increase energy, reduce fatigue, and improve muscle growth, strength, recovery, and athletic performance.

Clinical Studies:

This ingredient has been shown to improve performance in placebo-controlled studies with trained adults. Its Clinical Support Rating is 5 (5/5).

One placebo-controlled study examined the effects of ATP supplementation on exercise performance in a group of experienced weight-training men.[67] Subjects took either a high dose (225 mg) or low dose (150 mg) of ATP for 14 days. Measurements were taken at baseline, following the first dose, and at the conclusion of daily supplementation. Anaerobic performance was evaluated with Wingate testing on a stationary cycle ergometer, and bench press was used to evaluate strength. Most strength and performance variables reported no effect of supplementation, including bench press strength at 70% max, peak anaerobic power, average anaerobic power, total work, and post-workout lactate accumulation. There were, however, three statistically significant findings. These were a 6.6% increase in 1-rep max after a single dose, and an 18.5% increase in first set repetitions and 22% increase in total lifting volume after two weeks of supplementation compared to placebo. There was also a statistically strong increase in 1-rep max after two weeks. The researchers warned, however, that the ergogenic benefits were minor, inconsistently noticed, and came without a significant increase in serum ATP levels. There were also two subjects in the high dose group that had unusually strong positive responses in 1-rep max strength (statistical outliers) after the first dosing, which may have skewed the results. As such, the positive strength findings may be the result of methodological error.

A second study involved the administration of a single dose of either 100 mg or 250 mg of adenosine triphosphate to a group of healthy men and women. Oxygen saturation was measured by pulse oximetry, and blood flow to the extremities was examined with readings of ankle and brachial arterial pressure. The study demonstrated that there was a statistically significant increase in ankle (+ 4.45 mmHg) and brachial (+ 6.45 mmHg) pressure, as well as upper extremity oxygenation (+1.36%), one hour after administration of the 100 mg dose. This study suggests that ATP may be useful for improving oxygen delivery to the muscles, which could improve exercise performance.

Further research is needed to determine if there is substantial ergogenic value to the use of adenosine triphosphate by athletic individuals.

Empirical Evidence:

Adenosine triphosphate is not widely available as a stand-alone supplement, as it is most often incorporated into blended formulas. It is difficult to gather feedback on the use of this nutrient alone. An objective evaluation of ATP, based in part on user experiences, as well as those of other product developers, suggests that this supplement may have value in sports nutrition, but it is too early to know for certain. If an effect becomes obvious, it probably will not involve rapid increases in muscle size and strength, but mild increases in energy and endurance. Adenosine triphosphate presently has an Empirical Evidence Rating of 3 (3/5).

Effective Dosage:

Based on clinical studies, a daily dosage of 100-250 mg is recommended.

Side Effects / Safety:

Adenosine triphosphate was well tolerated during clinical studies with healthy subjects, with no significant side effects.

Alpha-Glycerylphosphorylcholine

syn. alpha-GPC
syn. choline alfoscerate

PERFORMANCE VALIDATION SCORES	
Combined	7
Clinical Support Rating	3
Empirical Evidence Rating	4

Description:

Alpha-glycerylphosphorylcholine (Alpha-GPC) is a naturally occurring choline-containing phospholipid metabolite. In supplemental form, this material is derived from soy lecithin. The main purpose of using alpha-glycerylphosphorylcholine is to supply the essential nutrient choline to the body. Choline is necessary for the biosynthesis of acetylcholine, a principle neurotransmitter. Alpha-GPC has been demonstrated to serve as a dietary precursor for acetylcholine, increasing levels of this neurotransmitter in certain regions of the brain upon supplementation.[68] Although alpha-glycerylphosphorylcholine is a naturally occurring compound, it is regulated as a drug in many countries outside of the United States due to its biological activity.

Acetylcholine plays an integral role in the functioning of both the central and peripheral nervous systems. This means that this neurotransmitter is closely involved with not only the mental aspects of exercise and athletic performance, but also the physical. This even includes the recruitment of individual muscle fibers for physical movement and strength,[69] and the flow of blood to the muscles.[70] In theory, an increase in the production of acetylcholine might yield a number of tangible benefits with regard to sports performance. The most prominent of these may include increased mental energy and focus during training, improved hand-eye coordination, enhanced muscle strength, and elevated growth hormone levels for improved muscle recovery and growth.

Promoted Benefits:

Alpha-glycerylphosphorylcholine is promoted to elevate growth hormone levels, and help increase muscle mass, strength, and athletic performance.

Clinical Studies:

This ingredient has been shown in human placebo-controlled studies to improve a metabolic marker (growth hormone) often linked to positive changes in body composition or performance. It has a Clinical Support Rating of 3 (3/5).

The most relevant study of interest examined the effect of alpha-glycerylphosphorylcholine on post-exercise growth hormone levels in a group of resistance-trained men.[71] Each subject was given a single 600 mg dose of the supplement, and then asked to perform six sets of squats at 70% of their one-rep maximum weight. Blood was sampled at baseline, and at several points up to two hours after the bout of exercise. Subjects taking Alpha-GPC noticed an approximate 70% higher peak level of growth hormone compared to those taking the placebo (8.4 vs. 5.0 ng/mL). Further study is necessary to see if extended supplementation will translate to tangible improvements in exercise performance.

Empirical Evidence:

Alpha-glycerylphosphorylcholine is widely available as a stand-alone supplement. The feedback on this supplement tends to be positive. A majority of users report an improved state of mental energy and alertnessas a result of supplementation. This is sometimes accompanied by perceived improvements in muscle mass, strength, and/or performance. Several colleagues that I know who have worked closely with this supplement share a positive view of its potential. Although a minority response, many other users are unable to attribute an increase in exercise performance to this supplement. It is possible that Alpha-GPC is capable of eliciting the desired positive changes to acetylcholine and growth hormone levels in users, but they are not always sufficient for short-term physical improvements. Alpha-glycerylphosphorylcholine has an Empirical Evidence Rating of 4 (4/5).

Effective Dosage:

Based on clinical studies, a dosage of 600-1,200 mg per day is recommended.

Side Effects / Safety:

Alpha-glycerylphosphorylcholine was well tolerated during one clinical study involving 2,044 patients taking up to 1,200 mg daily for six months.[72] Side effects were only reported in approximately 2% of patients. The most common of these were nausea, heartburn, insomnia, and headache.

Alpha-Ketoisocaproic Acid (KIC)

syn. 2-ketoisocaproate
syn. alpha-oxoisocaproate

PERFORMANCE VALIDATION SCORES	
Combined	**4**
Clinical Support Rating	2
Empirical Evidence Rating	2

Description:

Alpha-ketoisocaproic acid (KIC) is a natural metabolite of the branched-chain amino acid L-leucine. It is also a precursor to beta-hydroxy-beta-methylbutyrate (HMB).[73] Alpha-ketoisocaproic acid is involved in a number of biological activities that might lend itself to efficacious supplementation. For example, KIC has been shown to increase nitrogen retention and preserve muscle protein in studies with both animals and postoperative patients.[74,75] It has also been shown to spare the utilization of glucose, which may allow it to preserve muscle energy.[76] It may also reduce the buildup of ammonia, which could help maintain optimal muscle performance.[77] Unfortunately, studies on the use of alpha-ketoisocaproic acid as an isolated supplement in exercising adults have been very limited, and thus far not supportive.

Promoted Benefits:

Alpha-ketoisocaproic acid is promoted to improve exercise endurance, and support increased muscle size, strength, and performance.

Clinical Studies:

The use of alpha-ketoisocaproic acid as a sport supplement is supported by animal data only. Its Clinical Support Rating is 2 (2/5).

One study examined the effect of alpha-ketoisocaproic acid on the growth rate of lambs.[78] The animals were given the amino acid metabolite both via injection, and orally at varying dosages (1-15 g per animal). Animals supplemented with alpha-ketoisocaproic acid were noted to have greater gains in lean muscle tissue, accompanied by greater reductions in fat loss, compared to non-supplemented animals.

There has been one placebo-controlled study of the short-term supplementation of alpha-ketoisocaproic acid by resistance-trained men.[79] Subjects took a dose of either 1.5 g or 9 g of KIC immediately prior to exercise, which consisted of both upper and lower body resistance training (leg and chest press). During this study, alpha-ketoisocaproic acid failed to improve acute muscle performance. Whether the results may have been different after continued supplementation remains unknown.

Further research is needed to determine if there is any ergogenic value to the use of alpha-ketoisocaproic acid by athletic individuals.

Empirical Evidence:

Alpha-ketoisocaproic acid has not been widely used

as a stand-alone supplement. As a result, user feedback has been limited. Of the data available, the experiences from this supplement have been very mixed, but less than favorable. Some have noticed benefits to KIC supplementation, usually with improvements in muscle stamina. There are also a few reports of substantial muscle or strength gain. A slightly larger percentage of users find they are unable to attribute any specific performance or body composition benefit (muscle mass, strength, endurance) to its use. It is difficult to draw conclusions based on the strong divergence of opinion. Alpha-ketoisocaproic acid has an Empirical Evidence Rating of 2 (2/5).

Effective Dosage:
An effective dosage of this supplement has not been established. Manufacturers typically recommend 2-10 g per day.

Side Effects / Safety:
Alpha-ketoisocaproic acid was well tolerated during clinical studies, with no significant side effects reported.

Alpha-Lipoic Acid (ALA)

syn. Thioctic acid
syn. 2-dithiolane-3 penatanoic acid

PERFORMANCE VALIDATION SCORES	
Combined	7
Clinical Support Rating	3
Empirical Evidence Rating	4

Description:

Alpha-lipoic acid (ALA) is a sulfur containing vitamin-like antioxidant. It is obtained in the diet from a number of sources, including yeast, spinach, broccoli, potatoes, and meat.[80] The body can readily synthesize ALA as well, which means that it is not considered an essential nutrient. This also excludes any classification as a vitamin, even though it possesses some similarity to the B-complex family. Alpha-lipoic exerts a number of key biological activities that can support optimal metabolism. Its supplementation is commonly used for the support of numerous medical conditions including type-2 diabetes, metabolic syndrome, reduced cognitive function, heavy metal toxicity, and liver poisoning. Alpha-lipoic acid supplements are also used to support exercise, particularly energy and nutrient partitioning.

The mechanism of action for alpha-lipoic acid begins with its powerful antioxidant properties.[81] ALA is both a water- and fat-soluble substance. This allows it to act as a universal antioxidant, neutralizing free radical products of metabolism in both watery and fatty areas of cells (such as cell fluids and membranes). In contrast, the antioxidant vitamins C & E are only water and oil soluble (respectively), which limits their regions of activity. ALA may also protect these two antioxidant vitamins from metabolism, enhancing their activates. The antioxidant properties of alpha-lipoic acid may be additionally strengthened due to its own resistance to deactivation, as a primary metabolite of ALA (dyhydrolipoic acid, DHLA) also appears to have strong antioxidant activity.

Alpha-lipoic acid also exerts a strong influence over blood glucose management, although its exact mode of action in this process is not fully understood. Studies show that this nutrient can increase the sensitivity of skeletal muscle cells to the hormone insulin, responsible for stimulating the uptake of glucose into cells.[82] This occurs, at least in part, via an increase in insulin receptor protein content.[83] By increasing insulin sensitivity, the body is better able to drive nutrients into muscle cells, and away from storage in adipose (fat) cells, which is typically increased with insulin resistance and diabetes. Alpha-lipoic acid also appears to increase glucose uptake via insulin-independent mechanisms.[84]

With regard to energy metabolism, alpha-lipoic acid has a number of key activities important to the functioning of cell mitochondria, the principle sites of cellular energy production.[85] To begin with, ALA is a cofactor in several mitochondrial enzyme complexes. Among other things, it plays a key role in the citric acid (Krebs) cycle, which involves the oxidation of proteins, fats, and carbohydrates to produce adenosine triphosphate (ATP), the principle fuel for cells.[86] Studies also suggest that alpha-lipoic acid is able to protect the mitochondria from lipid peroxidation damage, and enhance electron transport chain complex (ETC) activities.[87] These effects, combined with an increase in glucose uptake, may result in an increase in overall energy storage in muscle cells.

It is important to note that alpha-lipoic acid exists in two enantiomer forms, an R isomer (R-ALA) and an S isomer (S-ALA). Supplement forms of ALA either come as pure R-ALA, or a mixture of both isomers, often in relatively equal quantities. Studies suggest that R-ALA is both better absorbed than S-ALA, and is also more biologically active.[88,89] With regard to insulin sensitivity, the S-isomer may even induce resistance to this hormone, countering some of the beneficial effects of R-ALA. While a majority of clinical studies on alpha-lipoic acid have involved the use of a mixture of both isomers, R-ALA is generally regarded as the preferred form of this nutrient to use for supplementation purposes.

If the metabolic effects of alpha-lipoic acid are consistently carried over into healthy exercise-experienced individuals, this nutrient may offer tangible ergogenic value. Of particular interest to bodybuilders and other resistance-trained athletes may be a positive nutrient partitioning effect, which could help support lean muscle gains and reduce fat retention. This nutrient might also be of interest to a wider range of athletes for its positive effects on energy metabolism and muscle endurance. While empirical evidence does support the use of ALA for certain performance-enhancement purposes, this nutrient has not been extensively studied in a clinical setting for such use. Its potential ergogenic properties remain speculative.

Promoted Benefits:
Alpha-lipoic acid is promoted to increase muscle insulin sensitivity and nutrient/energy storage.

Clinical Studies:
This ingredient has been shown in human placebo-controlled studies to improve a metabolic marker (insulin sensitivity) often linked to positive changes in body composition or performance. It has a Clinical Support Rating of 3 (3/5).

One controlled study examined the effects of alpha-lipoic acid in a group of patients with type-2 (non-insulin dependent) diabetes.[90] An oral dosage of 1,200 mg daily (taken in two 600 mg doses) was administered for a period of four weeks. At the end of supplementation, peripheral insulin sensitivity and glucose disposal were measured with the use of a two-hour hyperinsulinaemic euglycaemic clamp. This is a metabolic measuring technique that steadily infuses insulin along with enough glucose to maintain stable blood sugar levels. The study found that peripheral insulin sensitivity and glucose disposal were significantly increased with the supplementation ALA, and effectively matched levels of control subjects with normal blood glucose control.

Some animal studies support the potential ergogenic effect of alpha-lipoic acid with more detail. For example, one study examined the effects of a diet supplemented with R-ALA (30 mg/kg of body weight per day) in a group of obese rats.[91] The study ran for a period of six weeks. The protocols involved an evaluation of exercise capacity with the use of treadmill exercise. While maximum oxygen consumption (VO2max) did not change, the supplementation of alpha-lipoic acid was shown to increase maximum run time (exercise endurance) by 18%.

While these results support potential ergogenic action, further research is needed to determine if alpha-lipoic acid exhibits consistent performance-enhancing properties in trained adults.

Empirical Evidence:

Alpha-lipoic acid is widely available as a stand-alone nutritional supplement. The feedback on its use as a sport supplement tends to be positive. To begin with, the insulin sensitizing effect of ALA is widely reported and difficult to dispute. For a wide number of users, this reportedly assists with nutrient partitioning into muscle tissue, helping to retain more lean, and less fat, body mass. Very often it is taken both before and after training, in an effort to help shuttle nutrients to skeletal muscle tissue during the important recovery window after exercise. It is unknown if this offers any advantage to regular dosing throughout the day. Some users also report increased muscle endurance and energy, though this benefit appears to be less consistently noticed. A minority of users fail to notice any benefit with regard to the supplementation of alpha-lipoic acid. Whether this is due to an individual insensitivity to the supplement is unknown. Alpha-lipoic acid has an Empirical Evidence Rating of 4 (4/5).

Effective Dosage:

Based on clinical studies, a dosage of 600-1,800 mg per day (mixed R-ALA/S-ALA) is recommended. A dosage of 300-900 mg is recommended for the pure R-ALA form of alpha-lipoic acid.

Side Effects / Safety:

Alpha-lipoic acid was well tolerated during clinical studies, with few side effects reported. A small percentage of users notice dermatological issues (rash, itch, and skin allergy) and/or gastrointestinal distress (loose stool, nausea, diarrhea, vomiting). ALA may enhance the hypoglycemic effect of insulin drugs.

Androst-4-ene,3,6,17-trione (6-OXO)

syn. 4-Etioallocholen-3,6, 17-Trione
syn. 6-oxo-androstenedione

PERFORMANCE VALIDATION SCORES	
Combined	8
Clinical Support Rating	3
Empirical Evidence Rating	5

Description:

Androst-4-ene,3,6,17-trione (6-OXO) is a naturally-occurring metabolite/intermediary in androgen biosynthesis. Although no primary dietary source of this compound has been identified, it is found in trace amounts in some animal products. It has not been shown to have a necessary biological function, and is not considered an essential dietary nutrient. In humans, 6-OXO has been shown to inhibit the aromatase enzyme, which is responsible for converting testosterone and certain other steroid hormones to estrogens (such as estradiol and estrone). 6-OXO is widely sold in sports nutrition, where it is promoted to increase testosterone levels and augment the anabolic effects of resistance training in men.

6-OXO is classified as a Type-I inhibitor of aromatase.[92] It irreversibly binds the aromatase enzyme, preventing it from interacting with steroid hormones and producing estrogen. This can significantly increase serum testosterone levels by two mechanisms. First, feedback inhibition of testosterone biosynthesis from estrogen is reduced (the brain reads high es-

trogen as a sign of high testosterone).[93] Second, less free testosterone will be metabolized to estrogens, and thus left intact. Since testosterone is a strongly anabolic (muscle-tissue building) hormone in humans,[94] an increase in its levels might support an increase in muscle mass and strength.[95] The ergogenic benefits of testosterone increases within or near normal levels, however, remain speculative.

At the doses studied and recommended (300-600 mg per day), 6-OXO exhibits an incomplete level of aromatase inhibition. Estrogen levels tend to remain relatively stable (or even increase slightly) during treatment. This may be due to a new homeostatic balance being reached, with lower levels of aromatase being countered by increased availability of aromatizable substrates. Since estrogen has been shown to play a beneficial role with regard to the management of serum lipids and cardiovascular disease risk,[96] and aromatase inhibition with other drugs has been shown to negatively alter cholesterol levels in men,[97] significant estrogen suppression may actually not be as desirable.

Studies also suggest that 6-OXO can increase steroid metabolism by the 5-alpha reductase enzyme. This enzyme is responsible for converting testosterone to a more androgenic metabolite (dihydrotestosterone) in various androgen responsive target tissues such as the skin, scalp, and prostate. While DHT is speculated to impart beneficial effects with regard to exercise performance, it also is linked to the unwanted androgenic effects of steroid therapy (such as acne and male pattern hair loss). There have been, however, no reports in the cited clinical studies of significant androgenic side effects. The net metabolic effect of the DHT increase with 6-OXO remains unclear.

Clinical studies support the use of 6-OXO to increase free testosterone levels in recreationally-active men. Given the known importance of testosterone in the muscle anabolic process, it is speculated that 6-OXO can increase the rate of muscle accumulation in response to regular resistance exercise. While clinical studies have not evaluated the effects of this supplement on exercise performance, empirical evidence seems to strongly support such use. Further research is needed to confirm, and better understand, the potential ergogenic properties of 6-OXO.

Promoted Benefits:
6-OXO is promoted to increase testosterone levels in men, and support muscle and strength gains in response to resistance training.

Clinical Studies:
This ingredient has been shown in human placebo-controlled studies to improve a metabolic marker (free testosterone levels) often linked to positive changes in body composition or performance. It has a Clinical Support Rating of 3 (3/5).

There has been only one published placebo-controlled clinical study on the use of 6-OXO in exercising adults.[98] In this study, subjects consumed 300 mg or 600 mg of the supplement daily for a period of eight weeks. Body composition, hormone levels, and various markers of clinical safety were evaluated at baseline, and various points during and after supplementation. Subjects taking 300 mg and 600 mg noticed a 90% and 84% increase in free testosterone levels (respectively) compared to placebo. There was also a 192% and 265% increase in dihydrotestosterone with the 300 and 600 mg groups, respectively. Body composition (muscle, fat mass) did not change significantly. Given the methodological difficulties with proving body composition changes in small group clinical studies like this, it is difficult to draw conclusions based on this result. Unfortunately, exercise performance (which tends to be easier to quantify) was not evaluated.

These results support the use of 6-OXO to increase testosterone levels in healthy exercising men. However, further research is needed to confirm this is accompanied by consistent tangible ergogenic value.

Empirical Evidence:
6-OXO is widely available as a stand-alone nutritional supplement. The feedback on its use as a sport supplement has been strongly positive. Most users sensitive to changes in their hormone levels are able to attribute a tangible increase in relative androgenicity to the use of this supplement. For many, this is accompanied by a noticeable increase in the gains (strength, muscle mass) of regular resistance exercise. Testosterone boosters have become a strong class of dietary supplements in the sports nutrition market, and 6-OXO has solidified its position as one of the most reliable such products available. A small minority of users do feel they cannot attribute any positive changes in exercise performance to use of this supplement. Whether this is due to individual insensitivity to 6-OXO, or an inability of a moderate increase in free testosterone to effect substantial gains in some users, remains unclear. 6-OXO has an Empirical Evidence Rating of 5 (5/5).

Effective Dosage:
Based on clinical studies, a dosage of 300-600 mg per day is recommended.

Side Effects / Safety:

6-OXO was well tolerated during clinical studies, with no side effects reported. Furthermore, there were no negative changes in various markers of clinical safety including cholesterol levels, blood pressure, liver and kidney enzymes, and blood cell counts.

Arachidonic Acid (ARA)

syn. eicosa-5,8,11,14-enoic acid
syn. arachidonate

PERFORMANCE VALIDATION SCORES	
Combined	10
Clinical Support Rating	5
Empirical Evidence Rating	5

Description:

Arachidonic acid (ARA) is an omega-6 essential fatty acid (EFA). It is found in a variety of foods, most notably meats such as chicken, beef, duck, and lamb.[99] In the body, ARA serves as precursor to several hormone-like compounds including prostaglandins, leukotrienes, lipoxins, thromboxanes, and epoxyeicosatrienoic acids.[100] This makes ARA integral to many important biological functions including development, nutrient metabolism, neurological activity, immunity, inflammation, insulin signaling, bone mineral density, and vascular homeostasis.[101,102,103] Arachidonic acid is also necessary for the adaptive (growth) response to training.[104,105] In sports nutrition, arachidonic acid is widely used to increase muscle mass and strength, and improve performance in power-based sports.

The role of arachidonic acid in the process of muscle growth is not fully understood, although it is known to involve several levels of action. Much of its activity appears to be mediated by its conversion to the prostaglandins PGE2 and PGF2α within the skeletal muscles. These prostaglandins can shift local physiology in several ways that favor muscle anabolism. To begin with, they (principally PGF2α) increase the rate of protein synthesis.[106] This may be due in part to an enhanced local sensitivity to anabolic hormones such as IGF-1,[107] testosterone,[108] and insulin.[109] Prostaglandins may also support the satellite cell cycle, especially satellite cell proliferation.[110] This too is integral to muscle hypertrophy. Additionally, prostaglandins enhance nitric-oxide-mediated vasodilation, which can increase blood flow and nutrient delivery to the muscles, potentially aiding recovery.[111]

Arachidonic acid does not exist in an entirely free state in the body, and has a high affinity for storage in muscle cell membrane phospholipids.[112] It remains bound in these phospholipids until released (and then activated) by certain stimuli. The stretching of muscle fibers during physical activity and exercise serves as a primary trigger for the release of ARA from muscle cells, as well as its local conversion to PGE2 and PGF2α.[113] Given that prostaglandins are rapidly broken down in circulation, their actions are also much more localized than systemic (whole-body).[114] This allows arachidonic acid (through prostaglandins) to direct anabolic activity specifically to those local damaged tissues in need of repair. It may also explain why targeted resistance training is necessary to elicit a significant overall muscle-building effect (only the trained muscles tend to grow).

Regular exercise has been shown to lower the concentration of arachidonic acid in muscle tissue.[115] It has also been shown to reduce active prostaglandin synthesis during training.[116] Given how closely prostaglandins are tied to muscle growth, ARA reductions may work to diminish the anabolic response. Athletes with arachidonic acid depletion may, likewise, have a harder time triggering or maintaining an anabolic metabolism than those with normal levels. The supplementation of arachidonic acid has been shown to effectively increase phospholipid ARA storage.[117, 118] It may take a couple of weeks to significantly increase concentrations, however, suggesting that this nutrient has a loading period, somewhat similar to creatine.[119]

Arachidonic acid appears to have a very basic and central role in protein synthesis and muscle growth. Tissue concentrations of arachidonic acid can also be effectively increased with supplementation, suggesting a tangible ability for individuals to manipulate this rate-limiting step in the anabolic process. This seems to be in line with clinical and empirical evidence in support of a measurable ergogenic response to ARA supplementation. Presently, arachidonic acid appears to be a promising supplement for healthy individuals undergoing resistance training, or athletes in anaerobic/power sports. Whether or not arachidonic acid supplementation has any ergogenic effects in prolonged endurance exercise remains unknown.

Promoted Benefits:
Arachidonic acid is promoted to increase muscle size, strength, and performance during anaerobic/power activities.

Clinical Studies:
This ingredient has been shown to improve performance in placebo-controlled studies with trained adults. Its Clinical Support Rating is 5 (5/5).

Arachidonic acid has been the subject of one placebo-controlled study examining its effects on exercise performance.[120] It involved the administration of 1,000 mg per day (X-Factor) for 50 days to a group of experienced resistance-trained men. All subjects followed a controlled resistance-training program over the 50-day period, and were evaluated before, during, and after supplementation for changes in body composition, strength, and anaerobic performance. The use of arachidonic acid resulted in a statistically significant increase in peak anaerobic power (+600%) compared to placebo. There were also statistically strong trends of improvement in other markers of exercise performance including a 44% increase in bench press 1-rep max lift, a 223% increase in average anaerobic power, and a 250% increase in muscle endurance compared to placebo. While the arachidonic acid group did gain more lean muscle mass than the placebo group over the course of the study, the statistical associations were too weak to draw any conclusions.

These results support the use of arachidonic acid as an ergogenic aid with resistance training and anaerobic/power sports. Further research is needed to validate and better understand the full ergogenic potential of this omega-6 essential fatty acid when supplemented by exercising adults.

Empirical Evidence:
Arachidonic acid is widely available as a stand-alone nutritional supplement. The feedback on its use as a sport supplement has been strongly positive. ARA has become fairly popular with weight training individuals, and is usually said to impart a distinct anabolic effect. One informal trial of the supplement among members of a popular online community for bodybuilders found an average gain of about seven pounds following 50-days of use.[121] While the total weight gain with arachidonic acid appears to be in line with that of creatine supplementation for many users, it

may involve more substantial protein (and thus tissue) retention in comparison (ARA does not appear to have the same osmotic effect on cells). Some users do fail to notice significant gains with arachidonic acid supplementation, even when taking the nutrient during active resistance training. Whether this is due to an individual insensitivity to the supplement, or particular applications in which it is, and is not, metabolically useful remains unclear. For the sake of disclosure, I was responsible for the development of ARA as a sports nutrition product, and could be regarded as having some bias. Overall, arachidonic acid has an Empirical Evidence Rating of 5 (5/5).

Effective Dosage:
Based on clinical studies, a dosage of 1,000 mg per day is recommended. Manufacturers commonly recommend 200-1,000 mg per day. Arachidonic acid is generally taken for a maximum of eight weeks, followed by an equal period of time off (cycled).

Side Effects / Safety:
Arachidonic acid (in dosages of 1,000-1,500 mg per day for 50 days) has been well tolerated during several clinical studies, with no significant side effects reported. All common markers of health including kidney and liver function,[122] serum lipids,[123] immunity,[124] and platelet aggregation[125] appear to be unaffected with this level and duration of use. Furthermore, higher concentrations of ARA in muscle tissue may be correlated with improved insulin sensitivity.[126] Arachidonic acid supplementation by healthy adults appears to offer no toxicity or significant safety risk.

Many users do report an increase in delayed onset muscle soreness (DOMS) after exercise while taking arachidonic acid. Recovery may also be slightly delayed. This is generally regarded as a direct and expected effect of supplementation, however, rather than a side effect (potentially indicating an intensi-

fied anabolic response). A small percentage of users also notice dermatological issues (oily skin, acne), which may be related to increased androgen sensitivity.

Arachidonic acid supplementation under recommended guidelines by healthy individuals should not result in a pro-inflammatory effect. ARA is metabolized to a series of both pro-inflammatory and anti-inflammatory compounds.[127] Studies administering dosages between 840 mg and 2,000 mg of this fatty acid per day have shown no increase in markers of inflammation.[128, 129, 130, 131] Increased arachidonic acid levels in the body actually tend to be associated with lower levels of pro-inflammatory IL-6 and IL-1, and higher levels of anti-inflammatory tumor-necrosis factor-beta.[132] This may reduce inflammation under some conditions.

Arachidonic acid does still play a central role in inflammation related to many diseased states. How it is metabolized in the body dictates its inflammatory or anti-inflammatory activity. Individuals suffering from joint pains or inflammatory disease may find that arachidonic acid supplementation exacerbates symptoms, probably because it is being more readily converted to inflammatory compounds due to the condition. Likewise, arachidonic acid supplementation is not advised for individuals with a history of inflammatory disease, or that are in compromised health. It is also of note that while ARA supplementation does not appear to have pro-inflammatory effects in healthy individuals, it may counter the anti-inflammatory effects of omega-3 EFA supplementation.[133]

Arginine (free, salt, ester)

syn. 2-amino-5-guanidinopentanoic acid
syn. L-arginine (salt)

Description:

Arginine is a common dietary amino acid. It is classified as a conditionally essential amino acid, which means that while the body is normally capable of manufacturing enough to meet its metabolic needs, under certain conditions (such as protein malnutrition, burns, infection, rapid development, and hyperammonemia) arginine must be supplied in the diet.[134] It is also classified as a glycogenic amino acid, which means that it can be converted to glucose when energy demands require it. Similar to all of the 20 common amino acids, one of the most basic roles of arginine is as a building block for the synthesis of new proteins. It is also necessary for the biosynthesis of urea, which removes ammonia (a cell toxin) from the body.

Arginine has a diverse set of additional biological activities, some of direct interest for athletic performance.[135] For one, it is necessary for the production of nitric oxide. Nitric oxide is a potent vasodilator, relaxing the blood vessels and assisting blood flow and nutrient delivery. Arginine is also involved in the stimulation of the growth hormone axis. It is specifically believed to suppress a hormone called somatostatin, which acts to inhibit growth hormone release. Arginine is also involved with the synthesis of creatine phosphate, an important constituent of the muscle energy cycle. Because of the known involvement of arginine in these biological processes, it has been the subject of athletic supplementation for many years.

As a supplement, arginine is usually supplied as a free form amino acid (pure arginine), an arginine salt, or an ester. The most common arginine products include arginine hydrochloride, arginine aspartate, di-arginine malate, and arginine ethyl ester. These compounds likely have varying solubility, absorption, and distribution properties, but are all regarded as delivering utilizable arginine to the body. Studies examining the potential performance enhancing properties of arginine and its various salts have thus far yielded inconsistent results. More research is needed to determine the potential value of arginine as a performance-enhancing supplement.

Promoted Benefits:

Arginine is promoted to increase growth hormone levels and nitric oxide production, and support improvements in muscle mass, strength, and athletic performance.

Clinical Studies:

This ingredient has been shown to improve performance in placebo-controlled studies with untrained individuals. It has a Clinical Support Rating of 4 (3/5).

The growth hormone elevating properties of oral arginine supplementation have been well documented. For example, one commonly cited study examined the effects of arginine supplementation on a group of healthy young men.[136] A single dose of 7 g was taken both at rest and prior to exercise. The study demonstrated an approximate 115% increase in GH levels when arginine was taken at rest. Hormone levels peaked approximately 1 hour after ingestion, and remained elevated for 2-3 hours. When the dose was taken immediately before resistance exercise, however, the combination resulted in an inhibition of the normal exercise induced peak in GH secretion.

The growth hormone response to arginine also appears to be a dose dependant phenomenon. We see this in a study that examined varying doses of oral arginine (5 g, 9 g, and 13 g) on the GH response in a group of healthy adult men.[137] The study found that the highest peaks in GH level occurred with the 5 g and 9 g doses. The response with the 13 g dose was deemed insignificant. Why the higher dose of arginine failed to produce the same positive response remains unknown.

The effects of regular arginine supplementation on exercise performance have been less conclusive. One study in support of arginine supplementation examined the effect of a 3 g daily dose on exercise performance in a group of healthy untrained men.[138] The supplement was taken for a period of 15 days. The approximately 2-week loading period of L-arginine (at a modest dosage) resulted in an 8.5% increase in muscle endurance during training (isokinetic knee extension resistance to fatigue).

Another study looked at the effects of 1 g of arginine daily (combined with 1 g of L-ornithine, another amino acid) for five weeks by a group of healthy untrained adult men.[139] All were subject to a progressive resistance-training program at the same time. Those subjects taking the arginine/ornithine supplement noticed statically significant improvements in total and lean body mass compared to placebo. The supplemented subjects also noticed less tissue damage, as evident by lower levels of urinary hydroxyproline. Given the combined use of L-ornithine, however, we cannot conclusively attribute the benefits to arginine supplementation.

In contradiction to these results, another placebo-controlled study examined four weeks of arginine aspartate supplementation by a group of young male endurance athletes.[140] Both low dose and high dose groups were used for the study, which consumed arginine aspartate in a dose equivalent to 2.8 g and 5.7 g of free arginine per day. Neither dose produced significant differences in peak oxygen consumption, time to exhaustion, or hormone levels (growth hormone, testosterone, cortisol, glucagon) compared to placebo.

The effects of arginine supplementation on nitric oxide production and blood flow following exercise were also examined in two placebo-controlled studies, without supporting results. The first examined a 6 g daily dose of arginine, which was taken for three days.[141] The supplementation failed to produce a statistically significant increase in nitric oxide production during a cycle exercise test compared to placebo. There was also no change in peak or average muscle power. The second study looked more closely at blood flow parameters of resistance exercise after the ingestion of a single 7 g dose of arginine.[142] Supplementation failed to produce a statistically significant improvement in forearm blood flow.

With regard to the vasodilation ("pump") effect of arginine, studies suggest this might actually be a counterproductive goal unless additional amino acids are also consumed. One such study involved subjecting a group of healthy volunteers to a bout of lower body resistance exercise, with or without an arterial balloon catheter to maintain blood flow at the pre-exercise state (inhibiting the pump effect).[143] The study demonstrated a significant improvement in muscle protein synthesis and amino acid influx/efflux balance when blood flow was reduced. It is speculated that an enhanced blood flow may increase the gradient between the serum and intracellular space, actually drawing amino acids out of the cells. If arginine is to be taken before training for an enhanced pump effect, a complete blend of essential and non-essential amino acids should also be provided, to help ensure this results in muscle nutrient delivery and not depletion.

Whether the inconsistent results concerning the effects of arginine on exercise performance are due to individual variances, study methodological difficulties, or a true absence of consistent ergogenic benefits remains unclear. Further study is needed to determine the potential role of arginine in sport supplementation.

Empirical Evidence:

Arginine has been widely used as a stand-alone supplement. The feedback on this supplement has been very mixed. To being with, the use of arginine as a vasodilator has been very popular in recent years. I believe the fact that this effect has not been clinically validated underlines the methodological difficulties with many clinical studies, not an absence of effect. Indeed, I believe that had the subject of this empirical review been the general use of arginine products to enhance the pump effect, it would rate as consistently positive (4/5). As it stands, however, the overall use of arginine products to increase muscle mass, strength, or performance, whether the side focus is pump enhancement or GH elevation, are less consistent, and roughly balanced between positive and negative experiences. Arginine has an Empirical Evidence Rating of 3 (3/5).

Effective Dosage:

Based on clinical studies, a dosage of 3-9 g per day (free arginine, arginine hydrochloride) is recommended. Equivalent doses of di-arginine malate and arginine ethyl ester have not been established.

It is generally advised to limit intake to 8-12 weeks, followed by equal time off, as it is believed that chronic use of arginine products may upregulate the arginase enzyme, reducing nitric oxide production and the supplement's efficacy.

When taken before training to stimulate vasodilation ("pump"), it is advised to also consume protein or a mixture of essential and non-essential amino acids. When taken for its effect on growth hormone secretion, arginine should not be taken before exercise.

Side Effects / Safety:

Arginine was well tolerated during all clinical studies with healthy subjects, with no significant side effects reported.

Arginine Alpha-Ketoglutarate (AAKG)

syn. Arginine 2-oxoglutarate
syn. L-arginine α-ketoglutaric acid

PERFORMANCE VALIDATION SCORES	
Combined	9
Clinical Support Rating	5
Empirical Evidence Rating	4

Description:

Arginine alpha-ketoglutarate (AAKG) is a modified form of L-arginine, which has been bonded with alpha-ketoglutarate (a glutamine precursor). The body will metabolize this to free arginine and alpha-ketoglutarate. Arginine is a common dietary amino acid, with a diverse set of biological activities important to athletic performance.[144] It is involved in protein synthesis, the production of nitric oxide (necessary for vasodilation and nutrient delivery), the removal of ammonia, stimulation of the growth hormone axis, and the synthesis of creatine phosphate, an important constituent of the muscle energy cycle. Although the research concerning L-arginine as a single amino acid supplement is ongoing, it has been demonstrated to improve athletic performance in some contexts.

Alpha-ketoglutarate (AKG) is an intermediary in the Krebs energy cycle (also known as the citric acid cycle). This metabolic pathway is vital to all cells, and involves the conversion of carbohydrates, fats, and proteins into usable energy. The supplementation of alpha-ketoglutarate to animals has been shown to in-

crease exercise endurance.[145] Alpha-ketoglutarate may also positively influence protein metabolism and the anabolic/catabolic balance under some conditions.[146] AKG supplements may also reduce ammonia levels during high protein intake, or when there are problems with nitrogen detoxification. Alpha-ketoglutarate has additionally been sold to improve athletic performance, although evidence on this use is still inconclusive.

Promoted Benefits:

Arginine alpha-ketoglutarate is promoted to increase nitric oxide production, and improve muscle mass, strength, endurance, and athletic performance.

Clinical Studies:

This ingredient has been shown to improve performance in placebo-controlled studies with trained adults. It has a Clinical Support Rating of 5 (5/5).

One study involved the administration of arginine alpha-ketoglutarate to a group of resistance-trained men (aged 30-50 years).[147] The dose used was 12 g per day, representing 6 g of arginine and 6 g of alpha-ketoglutarate. The total daily dose was divided into three applications of 4 g each, which were supplied in the form of time-release caplets (NO2®, MRI). The supplementation period was eight weeks, during which time all participants were subject to a controlled resistance-training program. Subjects taking the time-release AAKG supplement noticed statistically significant improvements in bench press 1-rep max (+ 8.82 kg vs. + 2.67 kg), peak anaerobic power (+ 6%), time to peak power (+ 3%), and rate to fatigue (+ 8%) compared to placebo. This study supports the use of arginine alpha-ketoglutarate for improving resistance-training performance.

Empirical Evidence:

Arginine alpha-ketoglutarate has been widely used as a stand-alone supplement. The feedback on this supplement has been positive. The general response of consumers seems to support a strong vasodilation effect during training, which is often accompanied by a perceived increase in muscle endurance. Many also find that strength and muscle mass are improved after several weeks of supplementation. Some others report dissatisfaction with the supplement, usually claiming a lack of substantial improvement even when an enhanced-pump effect is noticed. This, however, seems to represent a minority of users. Arginine alpha-ketoglutarate has an Empirical Evidence Rating of 4 (4/5).

Effective Dosage:

Based on clinical studies, a dosage of 12 grams per day is recommended. It is generally advised to limit intake to 8-12 weeks, followed by equal time off, as it is believed that chronic use of arginine products may upregulate the arginase enzyme, reducing nitric oxide production and the supplement's efficacy.

Side Effects / Safety:

Arginine alpha-ketoglutarate was well tolerated during clinical studies, with no significant side effects reported in healthy subjects.

Beta-Alanine

syn. β-alanine
syn. 3-aminopropanoic acid

PERFORMANCE VALIDATION SCORES	
Combined	10
Clinical Support Rating	5
Empirical Evidence Rating	5

Description:

Beta-alanine (β-alanine) is a natural amino acid. It is a beta isomer of the non-essential amino acid alanine (L-β-alanine), although unlike this traditional amino acid beta-alanine is not used for the synthesis of proteins. Instead, its main function appears to be the synthesis of carnosine (β-alanyl-L-histidine), a dipeptide found in high concentrations in skeletal muscle. Carnosine has a number of important physiological activities in muscle tissue. It serves as a primary pH buffer, an antioxidant, and increases cellular sensitivity to calcium, which is a trigger in muscle contractions. Carnosine also helps protect muscle proteins from oxidation and glycation (the reaction of sugars with proteins).[148]

Beta-alanine supplementation can significantly increase the amount of carnosine in muscle tissue. This may improve muscle endurance and performance at high levels of exertion. This is believed to occur mainly via an intramyocellular pH-buffering effect. During intense physical activity, both aerobic and anaerobic energy cycles will use ATP (adenosine triphosphate) for energy. Part of these energy processes result in metabolic byproducts, including hydrogen ions. ATP-associated hydrogen ions are primarily responsible for the lowering of pH in muscle tissue during exercise, an effect that contributes to fatigue. Carnosine buffers the accumulation of hydrogen ions, helping to keep the muscles within an acceptable pH range for a longer period of time during exercise.

It is of note that L-carnosine itself is inefficient for increasing muscle carnosine levels. Studies show that even after the consumption of large doses, only modest amounts appear in the blood intact. Much of the dietary carnosine is broken down before reaching target tissues. The enzyme carnosinase is believed responsible for much of this metabolism. The amino acid L-histidine is also required for muscle carnosine biosynthesis. It already exists in muscle tissue at high concentrations relative to its need for this synthesis, however, and is therefore an inefficient dietary precursor for carnosine. Beta-alanine is the limiting substrate in muscle carnosine synthesis, and remains the most efficient nutrient of supplementation for increasing tissue carnosine levels.

Promoted Benefits:

Beta-alanine is promoted to increase tissue carnosine levels, serve as a pH buffer, enhance muscle endurance, increase muscle mass and strength, and improve aerobic and anaerobic performance.

Clinical Studies:

Beta-alanine has been the subject of extensive clinical study. This ingredient has been shown to improve body composition and performance in placebo-controlled studies with trained adults. Its Clinical Support Rating is 5 (5/5).

One of the most widely cited studies with regard to exercise performance and the muscle accumulation of carnosine involved the supplementation of 4-6.4 grams of beta-alanine for 10 weeks by a group of physically active male subjects.[149] The tissue examined for carnosine content was the vastus lateralis, the largest of the quadriceps muscles. Those subjects taking beta-alanine noticed statistically significant increases in muscle carnosine concentrations (+58.8% and +80.1% at 4 and 10 weeks), compared to no increase in placebo. Anaerobic exercise capacity also increased 13% and 16.2% at 4 and 10 weeks in subjects taking beta-alanine, compared to no significant change in placebo.

A second study examined the effects of beta-alanine supplementation on exercise performance and hormonal adaptations in a group of experienced resistance-trained men.[150] The supplement was administered for a period of 30 days, and at a daily dosage of 4.8 g. A regular resistance-exercise program was followed, which included 6 sets of 12 repetitions of the squat exercise at 70% of the 1-rep maximum weight. Subjects taking beta-alanine were able to perform 22% more repetitions at the end of the four-week program compared to subjects taking placebo. Anaerobic power was also significantly higher with beta-alanine use (98.4 versus 7.2 watts). There were no changes in testosterone, growth hormone, or cortisol concentrations.

Another study examined 30 days of beta-alanine supplementation in a group of college football players.[151] The dosage used was 4.5 grams per day. Supplemen-tation began three weeks prior to pre-season training, and continued for nine days during active training. Players taking beta-alanine noticed significantly higher training volume on the bench press exercise compared to those taking placebo. There was also a statistically strong trend of increased training volume for all resistance exercises. Subjective reports of fatigue were also significantly lower for athletes taking beta-alanine.

With regard to positive changes in lean body mass, we can reference a placebo-controlled study that examined the effects of six weeks of beta-alanine supplementation by a group of recreationally active young men.[152] The investigation involved a regular controlled high intensity interval-training (HIIT) program with stationary cycling. The dose of beta-alanine taken was 6 grams per day for the first three weeks, followed by 3 grams per day for the last three weeks. Subjects taking beta-alanine noticed a modest but statistically significant increase in lean body mass (+1 kg) after three weeks, compared to no change with placebo. There were also intermittent improvements in peak oxygen consumption (VO2peak) and time to exhaustion (VO2tte).

Empirical Evidence:

Beta-alanine is widely used as a stand-alone product. The empirical evidence on this supplement has been very positive. A strong majority of users believe they notice benefits from beta-alanine. This most commonly includes a significant increase in muscle endurance, which may be noticed by an ability to perform additional sets and repetitions during resistance training, or to maintain a high level of performance for longer periods of time with other athletic activity. Many associate the longer training sessions with greater levels of stimulation, and thus enhanced physical results from training (muscle growth, strength gains). Alternately, a small percentage of users are disappointed with this supplement, and do not feel it supports sports performance. Whether a certain population is physiologically unresponsive to beta-alanine supplementation remains unknown. Beta-alanine has an Empirical Evidence Rating of 5 (5/5).

Effective Dosage:

Based on clinical studies, a dosage of 3-6 grams per day is recommended. This dose should be divided into multiple smaller doses of 400-800 mg to avoid a strong incidence of paraesthesia (see side effects). Note that it may take several weeks to reach peak tissue saturation and effect.

Side Effects / Safety:

Beta-alanine was well tolerated during clinical studies, with no harmful side effects reported. This supplement tends to cause paraesthesia, however, which is a non-dangerous irritation of the skin. Paraesthesia is characterized as a flushing or prickling sensation, which usually begins in the head and migrates to the upper torso including the arms and hands, and after that the lower parts of the body. This side effect usually occurs within 15-20 minutes of ingesting a capsule or solution containing beta-alanine, and lasts for approximately one hour. Paraesthesia is not believed to have a detrimental effect on the body.

Paraesthesia is a dose-dependant phenomenon.[153] Approximately 25% of users report a mild occurrence when taking an 800 mg dose of beta-alanine. Higher individual doses increase the likelihood of paraesthesia onset, as well as the severity of symptoms. This side effect can become markedly unpleasant at an individual dose of 2,000-3,000 mg. When using a standard beta-alanine supplement, sensitive individuals are advised to take smaller doses (400-800 mg) several times throughout the day in order to stay below the threshold for paraesthesia. Paraesthesia onset can also be avoided with the use of a time-released formulation of beta-alanine.

Betaine

syn. trimethylglycine
syn. glycine betaine

PERFORMANCE VALIDATION SCORES	
Combined	8
Clinical Support Rating	5
Empirical Evidence Rating	3

Description:

Betaine is a naturally occurring derivative of the amino acid glycine (specifically tri-methyl glycine). It is found in a variety of foods, although its levels are especially high in spinach, wheat, beets, and shellfish. Betaine is an organic osmolyte, supporting cellular hydration and increased cell volume.[154] A principle biological role of this nutrient is to protect cells against dehydration, high salinity, and thermal stress. Betaine also appears to support aerobic and anaerobic energy production,[155] and is also involved in the biosynthesis of creatine.[156] It has been speculated that some of its potential performance-enhancing effects may come from increased stores of creatine phosphate in skeletal muscle.

Betaine is a significant dietary methyl donor, and has a strong role in the methionine cycle in the liver and kidneys. The insufficient intake of methyl donating compounds like betaine can produce a state of hypomethylation. This can result in elevated homocysteine concentrations, low S-adenosylmethionine levels, and reduced fat metabolism in the liver. Hypomethylation has also been linked to DNA damage, genetic instability, and carcinogenesis. As a strong methyl donor, betaine may reduce the risk of some forms of cancer in humans, as well as heart, vascular, and liver diseases. The daily intake of betaine from dietary sources typically ranges from 1 to 2.5 grams. Betaine can also be synthesized in the body from choline-containing foods.

Promoted Benefits:

Betaine is promoted to help increase muscle endurance and exercise performance.

Clinical Studies:

Several clinical studies support the use of betaine as a performance-enhancing supplement. The ingredient has been shown to improve performance in placebo-controlled studies with experienced resistance-trained adults. Its Clinical Support Rating is 5 (5/5).

One placebo-controlled investigation examined the effect of betaine on power and endurance measures in men with at least three months of resistance exercise experience.[157] Betaine (1.25g twice daily) supplementation for 15 days failed to produce significant changes in bench press, anaerobic power, or vertical jump performance. It did, however, produce a statistically significant improvement in muscle endurance during the squat exercise.

A second placebo-controlled study examined the effects of 14 days of supplementation by recreationally trained men.[158] While this study failed to produce statistically significant changes in bench press or squat repetitions, it did report statistically significant improvements in bench press throw power, bench press force, vertical jump power, and squat force.

A third placebo-controlled study examined the effect of betaine on running and sprinting performance in a high temperature environment.[159] Experienced male runners were hydrated with a betaine and carbohydrate drink, and asked to perform 75 minutes of treadmill running at 65% maximal oxygen consumption (Vo2max), followed by a sprint to exhaustion at 85% Vo2max. Although not statistically significant, trends of improvement were noted in sprint performance, with time to exhaustion increasing by an average of 32 seconds (16%).

Empirical Evidence:
Betaine is not widely available as a stand-alone supplement. It is difficult to gather feedback on the use of this nutrient alone. The limited available empirical evidence is mixed, with some users reporting positive results, and many others not noticing a benefit. Betaine has an Empirical Evidence Rating of 3 (3/5).

Effective Dosage:
Based on clinical studies, a dosage of 1.25 grams twice daily is recommended.

Side Effects / Safety:
Betaine appeared to be well tolerated in clinical studies, with no reported adverse effects.

Branched-Chain Amino Acids (BCAA)

syn. leucine, isoleucine, and valine

PERFORMANCE VALIDATION SCORES	
Combined	10
Clinical Support Rating	5
Empirical Evidence Rating	5

Description:

Leucine, isoleucine, and valine are known as branched-chain amino acids (BCAA). These amino acids are highly prominent in muscle, and account for 14-18% of its total amino acid content.[160,161] BCAAs are used as more than just components for building muscle proteins. These amino acids appear to directly influence protein metabolism, both by stimulating protein synthesis and inhibiting protein degradation.[162] BCAAs may also influence muscle energy metabolism,[163] support the immune system,[164] reduce fatigue,[165] and diminish post-exercise muscle soreness.[166] Exercise enhances the breakdown of BCAAs, which may increase dietary requirements.[167] Branched-chain amino acid supplements are widely used in sports nutrition to enhance muscle growth and recovery from intense exercise.

| leucine | isoleucine | valine |

Branched-chain amino acids appear to increase muscle protein retention via several mechanisms. To begin with, BCAAs (particularly leucine) have been shown to stimulate the anabolic signaling pathway mTOR, and as a result its downstream target protein p70 S6 kinase, which are considered integral to muscle hypertrophy.[168] BCAAs also result in the stimulation of eukaryotic initiation factor 4E-binding protein (4E-BP1) and extracellular signal-related kinase (ERK 1/2), also linked to positive adaptive responses to training. However, some of these effects may not be maintained by leucine alone, thereby, supporting the need for complete BCAA supplementation.[169] Human studies also suggest that BCAA supplementation might increase plasma growth hormone levels, another positive mediator of muscle protein synthesis.[170]

BCAAs also appear to be strong inhibitors of muscle protein catabolism. Exercise has been shown to increase both muscle protein synthesis and breakdown rates. When proper nutrition is supplied, the balance should favor protein synthetic processes and muscle growth. Still, reducing the level of protein breakdown may result in a higher net protein gain. Studies have shown that the supplementation of branched-chain amino acids before or during intense exercise can significantly reduce protein breakdown, resulting in a tissue sparing effect.[171,172,173] Other studies have shown that when BCAAs are taken before and after training, markers of muscle breakdown were reduced for up to five days following exercise.[174,175] This suggests that there is an extended (as opposed to only acute) anti-catabolic effect on muscle protein.

BCAAs are also involved in muscle energy metabolism, both as direct energy providers and by preserving other energy substrates. Unlike the standard amino acids, which are mainly oxidized in the liver, branched-chain amino acids are readily oxidized in the muscles for energy.[176] A portion of the energy expended during high intensity exercise comes from the oxidation of BCAAs. Adequate BCAA levels may enhance muscle energy production, increase carbohydrate availability, and preserve muscle and liver glycogen stores.[177] Branched-chain amino acids may also lower the buildup of lactate during exercise, which is known to reduce endurance and slow recovery.[178]

Clinical and empirical evidence supports the use of branched-chain amino acids with both aerobic and anaerobic exercise. When taken before or during a period of intense training, BCAAs appear to reduce the rate of protein degradation (helping to preserve muscle). Branched-chain amino acids also tend to improve muscle soreness and tissue recovery in the days following exercise. When taken with a standard protein and carbohydrate drink during the post-exercise recovery period, BCAA supplementation can also enhance total protein retention beyond the intake of a protein/carbohydrate drink alone. In summary, BCAAs may have a tangible role in increasing muscle mass and strength following weight training, and improving recovery and possibly even performance during endurance activities.

Promoted Benefits:
Branched-chain amino acids are promoted to increase muscle mass and strength, improve recovery and soreness following exercise, and enhance overall athletic performance.

Clinical Studies:
Branched-chain amino acids have been shown to improve performance in placebo-controlled studies with trained adults. They have a Clinical Support Rating of 5 (5/5).

One placebo-controlled study monitored performance improvements in trained athletes and the effects of BCAA supplementation in cross-country and marathon runners.[179] The supplement was taking during active exercise. While no improvements were noticed in the higher performing athletes, the use of branched-chain amino acids improved running performance in the slower group of marathon runners (3:05 - 3:30 run time) compared to the use of a placebo. It also appeared to increase the retention of amino acids in the muscles. Branched-chain amino acids also reduced signs of mental fatigue in the cross-country runners during a 30-km race.

Another placebo-controlled study found BCAA supplementation to improve exercise performance during heat stress in a group of healthy untrained men and women.[180] Each subject took the branched-chain amino acid drink (or a placebo) every 30 minutes during exercise, which consisted of cycle ergometer training at 40% peak oxygen consumption (VO2peak) until the point of exhaustion. The use of a branched-chain amino acid supplement resulted in a significant improvement in time to exhaustion compared to placebo (153.1 min versus 137 min), which represents a notable improvement in endurance performance.

An additional placebo-controlled study looked at the effects of acute and chronic BCAA supplementation on energy metabolism and exercise performance in a group of healthy untrained men.[181] The subjects took a dose of 14.4 grams per day for the acute part of the study, which was taken on two separate occasions before exercise evaluations (forearm grip exercise). BCAA supplementation was shown to significantly improve cardiovascular performance (respiratory quotient) compared to placebo in this part of the study. During the chronic supplementation study, 14.4 grams of BCAA were taken daily for 30 days. Here, the use of BCAAs significantly improved muscle strength (grip strength) compared to placebo, without significantly affecting muscle size.

Exercise studies with branched-chain amino acids have had conflicting results. Some have failed to find statistically significant improvements in exercise performance following supplementation[182, 183], or have found BCAAs to be comparable to the use of a simple carbohydrate supplement.[184] Whether these inconsistent results are due to individual variances, study methodological difficulties, or specific circumstances in which BCAAs can exert tangible ergogenic effects remains unclear. Further study is needed to better understand the potential role of branched-chain amino acids in improving exercise performance.

The positive effects of branched-chain amino acids on muscle protein kinetics following anaerobic exercise appear to be well supported. One commonly cited placebo-controlled study examined the effects of the branched-chain amino acid leucine on protein synthesis and retention following resistance training in a group of healthy untrained subjects.[185] The leucine was added to a whey protein/carbohydrate recovery drink. The study also examined the same protein/carbohydrate drink without leucine, as well as a carbohydrate only drink. The exercise protocols consisted of eight sets each of leg press and leg extensions, which were performed at an ~80% 1-rep maximum weight for approximately 8 reps each. Subjects consumed the supplemental drink every 30 minutes after training, for a total of 6 hours. Measures of protein kinetics were taken at various points over this 6-hour window. The BCAA-enriched drink resulted in the greater overall retention of muscle protein.

Empirical Evidence:
BCAAs have been widely used as stand-alone nutritional supplements. The feedback on this type of supplement as an ergogenic aid has been strongly positive. As a result of their high efficacy, branched-

chain amino acids have become very popular with many types of both power and endurance athletes. Most consistently, the supplement seems to decrease the total time for muscle recovery, as well as soreness levels. This allows for a more frequent training schedule, and greater level of stimulus in a variety of activities. With regard to weight training specifically, BCAAs have become very popular anabolic support supplements. In most instances, the user can attribute a greater level of muscle gain when adding BCAAs to their regular supplementation schedule. It is commonly taken prior to or during exercise to reduce muscle damage during training, and immediately after to support muscle recovery. A small percentage of users report insufficient results with BCAAs, usually finding that they work no better than regular protein. It may simply be that in some circumstances BCAAs fail to provide sufficient (noticeable) improvements. Overall, branched-chain amino acids have an Empirical Evidence Rating of 5 (5/5).

Effective Dosage:
Based on clinical studies, a dosage of 5-20 g per day is recommended. BCAA supplements typically contain a similar amino acid balance to that found in animal proteins, consisting of a 2:1:1 ratio of leucine, isoleucine, and valine.

BCAAs can be taken before or during training to reduce muscle catabolism during exercise, or after training to support recovery. It may be most effective to supplement BCAAs both at the onset of (or during) exercise, and during the post-exercise recovery period.

Side Effects / Safety:
Branched-chain amino acids were well tolerated during clinical studies, with no significant side effects reported. Higher doses may cause gastrointestinal distress (nausea, diarrhea etc.).

Caffeine

syn. 1,3,7-trimethylxanthine
syn. methyltheobromine

PERFORMANCE VALIDATION SCORES	
Combined	10
Clinical Support Rating	5
Empirical Evidence Rating	5

Description:

Caffeine is classified as a central nervous system (CNS) stimulant. It belongs to a broad category of physiologically active molecules called alkaloids. Caffeine is specifically a methylated alkaloid of the xanthine family, sharing structural and functional similarity to other drugs of the class including paraxanthine, theophylline, and theobromine. As with other xanthines, caffeine is known for possessing mild (as opposed to strong) stimulant properties. It is typically described as providing increased physical energy, mental alertness, and excitability, but not euphoria. Although widely identified as a drug, caffeine is naturally occurring in many plants-based foods including tea, coffee, guarana, cocoa, and cola. It is the most widely consumed of all stimulants, with estimates suggesting that nearly 90% of the adult U.S. population use caffeine on a regular basis.

Caffeine is rapidly absorbed from the digestive tract, usually reaching peak effect 15-60 minutes after administration. It has a moderate duration of activity, exhibiting a plasma elimination half-life of 2.5 to 4.5 hours. Caffeine's primary mechanism of action involves antagonism (blocking) of adenosine A1 and A2A receptors in the brain.[186] Adenosine has CNS depressing activities, slowing down the firing rate of neurons. It is known to influence the release and activity of the neurotransmitters dopamine and acetylcholine. By antagonizing adenosine, caffeine facilitates both dopaminergic and cholinergic neurotransmission. It may also influence the secondary cellular messenger cyclic adenosine monophosphate (cAMP), as well as prostaglandin biosynthesis.[187] Additionally, caffeine has a mild diuretic effect, reducing the reabsorption of water by the kidneys.[188]

As a sports supplement, caffeine is usually taken immediately before exercise or an athletic competition, so as to provide a short-term boost in energy during the activity. Its ability to increase mental alertness makes it useful for many sports, but especially those requiring more focus. More than that, however, caffeine is known to increase motor activity. This means that it may actually enhance the control of muscle contraction. This is, of course, another key activity that might serve to improve athletic performance under some situations. Caffeine might also support bodybuilding and sports performance efforts indirectly, by allowing the individual to practice and exercise harder, with more mental and physical intensity, so that training is ultimately more productive. The individual response to caffeine may vary.

Promoted Benefits:

Caffeine is promoted to increase mental alertness, focus, physical energy, endurance, and overall sports performance.

Clinical Studies:

Caffeine has been the subject of extensive clinical study. It has been shown to improve performance in placebo-controlled studies with trained adults. Its Clinical Support Rating is 5 (5/5).

One placebo-controlled study examined the effects of varying doses of caffeine on exercise performance in a group of trained cyclists.[189] The subjects took one of three doses, 1 mg/kg, 2 mg/kg, or 3 mg/kg of bodyweight per day prior to exercise. The exercise consisted of a baseline ride on a stationary cycle ergometer at 80% oxygen consumption. This was followed by a 4-min recovery break, and then a 15-min VO2peak performance trial. The performance trial was initiated 60 minutes after ingestion of caffeine or a placebo. The subjects taking the 2 mg/kg and 3 mg/kg doses of caffeine noticed a 4% and 3% improvement in performance during the trial (respectively), while the 1 mg/kg dose had no effect. The improvements varied a great deal between individuals, with some noticing very strong, and some only minor, benefits from caffeine supplementation.

Another placebo-controlled study looked at the effects of caffeine in a group of medium distance runners.[190] The subjects used a dosage of 3 mg/kg of bodyweight, which was taken 60 minutes prior to an 8 km race on a track. Compared to placebo, subjects taking caffeine noticed a 1.2% improvement in performance, which amounted to a 23.8s faster run time in comparison. Individual improvements ranged from 10 to 61 seconds of improvement in time. Heart rate was higher in the caffeine group, although the subjective ratings of perceived exertion (RPE) were lower.

Another placebo-controlled study examined the effects of caffeine in a group of male and female competitive swimmers.[191] The subjects took a set dose of 250 mg, which on average equated to about four milligrams of caffeine per kilogram of bodyweight (4 mg/kg). It was taken 60 minutes prior to a swimming race, which consisted of two 100-meter sprints separated by 20 minutes. The subjects taking caffeine noticed enhanced swimming velocity in both races compared to those taking placebo. The caffeine also prevented a decrease in velocity between the first and second race, which was noticed in those taking placebo.

These and many other clinical studies support the use of caffeine to enhance performance in a variety of sports. These include endurance activities, sports requiring intermittent bursts of exertion such as team and racquet sports, and sports where sustained high intensity activity for up to 60 minutes is required, such as swimming, rowing, and middle to long distance running.[192] Further research is needed to better understand all of the athletic activities in which caffeine may impart a clear ergogenic effect, and how to best utilize this agent when a positive effect may be noticed.

Empirical Evidence:

Caffeine is a widely used sports supplement. The feedback on its use has been strongly positive. A majority of users report some benefit with regard to mental and physical energy, focus, endurance, and overall performance. Given the predominance of such positive reports, caffeine has become an extremely popular agent for providing pre-exercise or pre-event energy. For a small percentage of users, however, the stimulant properties of caffeine do not equate to any noticeable change in performance. Whether this is due to individual unresponsiveness to its ergogenic effects, or specific athletic circumstances in which caffeine may impart a beneficial effect, remains unclear. Some people are also very sensitive to the effects of caffeine, and find that its side effects outweigh its benefits. Overall, caffeine has an Empirical Evidence Rating of 5 (5/5).

Effective Dosage:

Based on clinical studies, a dosage of 3 mg/kg (bodyweight) of caffeine taken 15-60 minutes prior to an athletic event is recommended. This equates to about 200-250 mg for a person weighing 150-185 pounds. Studies suggest this caffeine imparts its peak effect at this moderate dosage level. Higher doses are unlikely to improve performance further, and are more likely to induce side effects. Note that coffee is not considered a good source of caffeine for improving performance, as the caffeine dosage can be very inconsistent.

Side Effects / Safety:

A moderate intake of caffeine (400 mg per day or 6 mg/kg of bodyweight) by healthy adults is generally considered safe, and devoid of significant side effects. Higher doses may be associated with side effects including nervousness, jitters, dizziness, elevated heart rate, and impaired performance.[193]

Carnitine

syn. 3-hydroxy-4-trimethylammoniobutanoate
syn. Levocarnitine (L-carnitine)

PERFORMANCE VALIDATION SCORES	
Combined	7
Clinical Support Rating	5
Empirical Evidence Rating	2

Description:

Carnitine is a vitamin or amino acid like compound produced in the body from lysine and methionine. It is found almost exclusively in muscle tissue.[194] Carnitine is not directly utilized for the synthesis of tissue proteins like its constituent amino acids. Instead, it plays an important role in the muscle cell energy cycle, where it is involved in the metabolism of fatty acids for fuel. Carnitine is found in a wide variety of foods, although the most prominent dietary sources include meat and dairy products. Since the body can readily manufacture carnitine from common amino acids, it is considered a conditionally essential nutrient, which means that it is essential in the diet only under certain metabolic conditions.[195]

Carnitine has a few primary roles with regard to cellular metabolism.[196] One is to assist in the transport of long chain fatty acids into the mitochondria of muscle cells. Carnitine does this by binding with long chain fatty acids, forming combined molecules called acylcarnitines that can readily transit the inner mitochondrial membrane. Once inside these cellular energy producers, these fats can be combined with oxygen to yield the most basic cellular energy source, adenosine triphosphate (ATP). The oxidation of fatty acids is a major source of fuel during exercise.[197] Carnitine also helps remove short chain fatty acids from the mitochondria, which can inhibit energy metabolism as they accumulate. Additionally, carnitine may serve as an antioxidant, helping to buffer some of the free radical products of cell metabolism.[198]

As we age, levels of carnitine tend to decline.[199] It is theorized that this may be involved in an age-related reduction of metabolic efficiency. Studies suggest that the supplementation of carnitine (or its derivatives) may improve energy metabolism in the elderly.[200] Carnitine supplements might also help treat a number of health conditions, including heart disease, Alzheimer's disease, HIV infection, diabetes, renal disease, cancer, and male infertility.[201] Research in this area is ongoing. Comparative studies suggest that carnitine and acetyl-L-carnitine are similar in their abilities to increase serum carnitine levels, though acetyl-L-carnitine appears to have a broader range of biological activity, particularly in the central nervous system.[202]

Given the importance of this nutrient in the muscle cell energy cycle, carnitine has long been the focus of supplementation by bodybuilders and athletes. Clinical studies and anecdotal evidence on such use, however, are highly conflicting. This may be due, in part, to difficulties overcoming the body's normal regulation of tissue carnitine content.[203] This supplement has been shown in some studies to improve performance in individuals with training experience, and thus has achieved the highest level of clinical validation. In a practical sense, however, tangible improvements are inconsistent. It seems most reasonable to conclude that this supplement may offer ergogenic value in situations where minor changes in maximal oxygen consumption could result in significant improvements in competition performance.

Promoted Benefits:
Carnitine is promoted to increase muscle stamina, and improve overall sports/exercise performance.

Clinical Studies:
Carnitine has been the subject of extensive clinical study. This ingredient has been shown to improve performance in placebo-controlled studies with trained adults. Its Clinical Support Rating is 5 (5/5).

One of the most compelling placebo-controlled studies with a positive response examined the effects of both acute and extended supplementation of carnitine in elite male and female athletes (kayak, rowing, and weightlifting).[204] All participants were subject to a controlled training and dietary program. Individuals in the extended supplementation group consumed 3 grams of carnitine daily for 21 days. The acute study involved a single dose of 4 grams. Supplemented subjects in the extended group noticed improvements in both the strength index and VO2max (maximal oxygen consumption) scores compared to placebo. There were also metabolic improvements with regard to serum free fatty acids and triglyceride levels. The acute study produced similar improvements in fatty acid and triglyceride metabolism 90 minutes after ingestion, as well as in distal latency (a measure of the time between muscle stimulus and muscle response).

A second placebo-controlled study examined the effects of carnitine supplementation on exercise performance in a group of trained endurance athletes.[205] Supplementation consisted of 2 grams of carnitine daily for 28 days. Baseline and end of study testing involved 45 minutes of stationary cycling at 66% VO2max. Subjects taking carnitine noticed a statistically significant reduction in respiratory quotient (RQ) compared to those taking placebo, which represents the ratio of carbon dioxide exhaled to oxygen consumed. The RQ helps determine the level and source of energy consumption (fat versus carbohydrate oxidation), and drops as fats become more readily utilized. Although not reaching statistical significance, there was also a strong trend of improvement in VO2max with the use of carnitine. These results suggest a notable improvement in the oxidation of fat for energy during exercise as a result of carnitine supplementation. This is a desirable result for exercise performance, as it can help spare glycogen and ATP reserves.

Another placebo-controlled study examined the effects of acute carnitine supplementation in a group of moderately trained men.[206] Subjects consumed 2 grams of carnitine or placebo one hour prior to exercise. The exercise protocols involved the use of a stationary cycle ergometer, which had its level of resistance increased by 50-W every three minutes until the point of exhaustion. In this study, the supplementation of carnitine was shown to produce statistically significant improvements in VO2max and power output. There were also reductions in total oxygen uptake, carbon dioxide production, pulmonary ventilation, and serum lactate, all suggesting improvements in metabolic efficiency with the supplementation of carnitine.

We also find performance benefits in a study of carnitine supplementation by a group of elite endurance walkers.[207] Subjects consumed four grams of carnitine daily for a period of 4 weeks, and were evaluated during a 120 minute walk at 65% of maximal oxygen consumption (VO2max). The supplementation of carnitine was shown to improve maximal oxygen consumption by 6%. There were, however, no statistically significant changes in blood lactate, ventilation, total oxygen consumption, or respiratory quotient. This study was not placebo controlled.

In contrast to the above studies, there have been many clinical investigations that have failed to produce statistically significant improvements in exercise performance following carnitine supplementation.

For example, one study with long distance runners found no improvements in marathon time, carbohydrate metabolism, fat metabolism, or serum lactate following a single dose of 4 grams of carnitine prior to a race.[208] There was also no change in a submaximal exercise performance test that was given the day after the race.

Eight healthy male athletes were given 4 grams daily for 14 days in another study.[209] While the supplementation resulted in an increase in the serum level of carnitine, it failed to produce any changes in muscle carnitine concentrations or serum lactate levels. This study was not placebo controlled.

Another investigation gave 6 grams of carnitine daily for 7-14 days to a group of healthy men.[210] Exercise performance was evaluated with 60 minutes of cycling at 70% maximal oxygen consumption. The supplementation of carnitine failed to produce any improvements in respiratory quotient, oxygen consumption, free fatty acids, or glucose utilization during exercise. Muscle carnitine levels did not change.

Exercise performance was evaluated following carnitine supplementation in another study with a group of elite male swimmers.[211] Subject consumed 4 grams of carnitine daily for seven days. In this study, carnitine supplementation did not result in any improvements in swimming performance or lactate concentrations compared to those taking placebo.

A group of moderately trained men were given 5 grams of carnitine per day for five days in another investigation. Exercise capacity was evaluated before and after supplementation with a stationary cycle ergometer, which was operated for 120 minutes at 50% maximal oxygen consumption. In this study, carnitine failed to produce statistically significant improvements in oxygen consumption or fatty acid turnover.

There are many additional clinical studies on the effects of carnitine supplementation on exercise performance in healthy adults, with varying results.[212] It is unclear if this high level of inconsistency is the result of methodological difficulties (statistical significance can be difficult to reach, especially in studies with trained athletes), dietary or training factors that influence the retention of carnitine in muscle tissue, or a situation where carnitine is only of ergogenic value when used under a very specific set of metabolic or athletic conditions. Further research is needed to better understand the optimal methods for utilizing L-carnitine to improve exercise performance in trained adults.

Empirical Evidence:

Carnitine is widely available as a stand-alone nutritional supplement. Unfortunately, the feedback on its use as a sport supplement tends to be negative. Most people that invest in carnitine do not find that its use results in noticeable improvements in exercise performance. This is especially true when the desired result is an increase in lean muscle mass or strength, a popular claim used by manufacturers in their advertising. A minority of users, however, do feel that carnitine offers value as a sport supplement, usually with regard to endurance exercise stamina. Given the results of placebo-controlled studies, it is reasonable to conclude that some of these reports are genuine. It may simply be that carnitine is an effective supplement, but only for a subset of users best positioned to notice its benefits, such as runners or other track and field athletes with very specific performance measures to work against. Carnitine has an Empirical Evidence Rating of 2 (2/5).

Effective Dosage:
Based on clinical studies, a dosage of 2-4 grams per day is recommended.

Side Effects / Safety:
Carnitine was well tolerated during clinical studies, with few side effects reported. A small percentage of users appear to notice gastrointestinal distress (loose stool, nausea, diarrhea).[213]

Cissus Quadrangularis

syn. vitis quadrangularis
syn. veld grape

PERFORMANCE VALIDATION SCORES	
Combined	6
Clinical Support Rating	3
Empirical Evidence Rating	3

Description:

Cissus quadrangularis is a vine producing plant of the vitaceae family, found natively throughout West Africa and Southeast Asia. Cissus has a long history of use in traditional Indian (Ayurvedic) medicine, where it has been applied as a pain reliever and wellness tonic, and to treat a number of medical conditions including asthma, menstrual irregularities, indigestion, heart burn/acid reflux, and parasitic worms. Cissus quadrangularis contains a number of different active components including flavonoids, vitamin C, carotene, ketosteroids, calcium, and beta-sitosterol. In sports nutrition, cissus quadrangularis products are promoted to increase muscle mass and strength, and reduce joint/tendon pain associated with heavy lifting or exercise.

Cissus quadrangularis is known to exert several different biological activities. To begin with, studies support its analgesic properties, and suggest they may be caused by the inhibition of arachidonic acid metabolism.[214] This is also the target of NSAIDs (non-steroidal anti-inflammatory drugs) such as ibuprofen. In-vitro studies also suggest it has potent antioxidant and free radical savaging properties. It may also have an immunomodulatory effect,[215] and possess anti-microbial properties (capable of killing certain bacteria).[216] Cissus quadrangularis has also been shown to support the mucous lining in the gastrointestinal tract, potentially protecting against ulcers.[217] It may also have acetylcholine-like actions in the central nervous system.[218]

With regard to its potentially beneficial effects on metabolism, human studies have shown that cissus quadrangularis can support reductions in adipose (fat) mass. Although its exact mechanism of action is not understood, in-vitro studies have shown it to inhibit amylase, an enzyme involved in the breakdown of starch into sugar.[219] It was also shown to inhibit the enzyme lipase, which is involved in the breakdown and transport of dietary fat. Cissus quadrangularis has also been shown to increase bone mineral density, counteracting the catabolic actions of cortisol.[220] It has been theorized this may extend to muscle anabolic or anti-catabolic properties, although no definitive studies in humans have yet been conducted to determine if such activities are present.

Promoted Benefits:

Cissus quadrangularis is promoted to block the catabolic effects of cortisol, and increase lean muscle mass and strength.

Clinical Studies:

Cissus quadrangularis has been shown in human placebo-controlled studies to improve a metabolic marker (creatinine levels) often linked to positive changes in body composition or performance. It has a Clinical Support Rating of 3 (3/5).

One placebo-controlled study examined the effects of cissus quadrangularis extract on body fat and markers of oxidative stress in obese men and women.[221] Each subject consumed 300 mg of cissus quadrangularis per day for eight weeks. There was no exercise involved in this study, although some subjects were subject to dietary (caloric) restrictions. The supplementation of cissus was shown to cause significant reductions in body weight and body fat percentage, supporting its use as a weight-loss supplement. Cissus was also shown to produce beneficial improvements in serum cholesterol, triglyceride, and glucose levels.

Contrary to common representations, this study did not report lean body mass measurements for the subjects. It did, however, measure serum creatinine levels. The major endogenous source for creatinine is the metabolism of creatine in the muscles. Because of this, creatinine is sometimes used as an indirect marker of muscle mass (its level correlating closely with the amount of muscle mass needed to produce it).[222] Researchers theorize this might represent a muscle anabolic effect. It remains unclear, however, if the body composition changes induced by cissus quadrangularis in this study actually included the retention/increase of skeletal muscle.

Peer reviewed placebo-controlled studies examining the effects of this supplement on skeletal muscle mass and exercise performance have not been published. Further research is needed to determine if cissus quadrangularis has ergogenic effects in humans.

Empirical Evidence:

Cissus quadrangularis is widely available as a stand-alone nutritional supplement. The feedback on its use as a sport supplement has been very mixed. The analgesic properties of this supplement appear to be well supported. Cissus is becoming highly valued for its ability to reduce joint and tendon pain, with many bodybuilders and athletes in contact sports now using it as a natural alternative to over-the-counter pain medications. This benefit, however, has unfortunately not coincided with common anecdotal reports of noticeable muscle and strength gain, or improved exercise performance. While many users do report such activity, this does not occur with enough frequency to consider it a positive trend. As an ergogenic aid, cissus quadrangularis has an Empirical Evidence Rating of 3 (3/5).

Effective Dosage:

An effective dosage of this supplement has not been established. Manufacturers commonly recommend 1,000-3,000 mg of cissus quadrangularis per day. Note there are various extracts of different standardization potencies.

Side Effects / Safety:

Cissus quadrangularis appeared to be well tolerated during clinical studies, with no significant side effects reported.[223]

Citrulline Malate

syn. citrulline malic acid salt
syn. L-citrulline-DL-malate

Description:

Citrulline malate (CtM) is the malic acid salt of citrulline, a naturally occurring nonessential alpha amino acid. Citrulline is not used directly in the assembly of tissue proteins like the 20 common amino acids, but instead is involved with other important functions including metabolic byproduct removal and cellular energy metabolism. Citrulline is found in many fruits, though its levels are particularly high in watermelon. In Europe, citrulline malate is sold as a medicinal product under the Stimol brand name (Gentilly, France). It is widely used to treat fatigue, and as a general energy tonic. In the United States and other regions with strong sports nutrition markets, citrulline malate is commonly sold to improve muscle endurance and aerobic exercise performance.

To understand the mode of action for citrulline malate, we can examine its two constituents. Citrulline serves as an intermediary in the urea cycle, which is necessary for the excretion of ammonia, a toxic byproduct of anaerobic metabolism. Citrulline is also a precursor to arginine, and may have some role in vasodilation.[224] This action may help increase blood flow to the muscles, facilitating oxygen and nutrient delivery. Malic acid may also provide an additional active component, as an intermediary in the citric acid (Krebs) cycle. This system is vital to aerobic metabolism, and facilitates the conversion of proteins, fats, and carbohydrates into useable cellular energy (ATP). The full spectrum of activity for citrulline malate likely involves the interaction of both of these components.

Many of the beneficial properties of citrulline malate are well supported. For example, CtM has been clearly documented to help combat general fatigue in humans.[225] It may also help stabilize the acid/base balance,[226] which could help the muscles maintain an optimal pH range for performance. The exercise-induced buildup of ammonia and lactate are also significantly reduced with the supplementation of citrulline malate[227] (both ammonia and lactate are implicated in exercise fatigue). CtM supplementation may also increase cellular ATP levels, the main form of stored cellular energy. Again, this could allow citrulline malate supplementation to improve exercise performance by helping to maintain optimal energy production. Citrulline malate appears to be a promising ergogenic supplement in both aerobic and anaerobic conditions.

Promoted Benefits:
Citrulline malate is promoted to increase energy, improve aerobic and anaerobic exercise endurance, and support vasodilation.

Clinical Studies:
Citrulline malate has been shown in human placebo-controlled studies to improve metabolic markers (ammonia, lactate) often linked to positive changes in body composition or performance. It has a Clinical Support Rating of 3 (3/5).

The most widely referenced study of citrulline malate and exercise involved its supplementation by a group of inactive (sedentary) male subjects complaining of fatigue.[228] Subjects consumed 6 g of citrulline malate per day for a period of 15 days. Exercise was conducted for evaluations of metabolic response at various points in the experiment, which involved finger flexions for 1.5-second intervals while lifting a 6 kg weight. Subjects taking CtM noticed a significant reduction in perceived fatigue, an increase in oxidative ATP production during exercise (+34%), and an increase in the rate of phosphocreatine replenishment (+20%) after exercise compared to their unsupplemented measurements. These results suggest citrulline malate can increase energy production during exercise. This study was not placebo-controlled.

The above study adds support to two prior placebo-controlled investigations involving the use of citrulline malate by sedentary individuals. These studies demonstrated significant reductions in serum lactate and ammonia levels when citrulline malate was supplemented prior to exercise.[229,230] Although performance measures were not taken as part of these investigations, the results would likely cause some attenuation of normal exercise fatigue.

These studies suggest that citrulline malate may improve exercise performance, especially with regard to anaerobic endurance-type activities. Further research is needed to confirm significant ergogenic value with regular supplementation by experienced exercising individuals.

Empirical Evidence:
Citrulline malate is widely available as a stand-alone nutritional supplement. The feedback on its use as a sport supplement tends to be positive. A majority of users seem to report noticeable benefits with regard to energy and muscle endurance. In aerobic/endurance-type activities, it seems to allow for high-level performance for longer periods. Although less consistent, many involved in resistance-training programs also find CtM to be of value, reporting an increase in anaerobic muscle endurance (generally equating to more sets and/or reps during training). A minority of users do fail to notice even minor benefits to using citrulline malate. It is unknown if this is due to the influence of training or dietary factors, or individual insensitivity to CtM. Citrulline malate has an Empirical Evidence Rating of 4 (4/5).

Effective Dosage:
Based on clinical studies, a dosage of 6 g per day is recommended.

Side Effects / Safety:
Citrulline malate was well tolerated during clinical studies, with no significant side effects.

Coleus Forskohlii Extract

syn. Forskolin
syn. Pashanabhedi

PERFORMANCE VALIDATION SCORES	
Combined	**6**
Clinical Support Rating	3
Empirical Evidence Rating	3

Description:

Coleus forskohlii, also known as plectranthus barbatus or Indian coleus, is an herbal plant of the mint family. It has a long history of use in traditional Indian (Ayurvedic) medicine, where it has been applied to treat such conditions as heart disease, convulsions, spasmodic pain, and painful urination.[231] Modern studies confirm this is a pharmacologically active plant, and suggest its extracts might have beneficial properties with regard to a number of health conditions including asthma,[232] arterial disease,[233] heart disease,[234] obesity,[235] and glaucoma.[236] Research is ongoing. In the field of sports nutrition, coleus forskohlii extracts are promoted to increase testosterone levels in men, and support enhanced strength and muscle mass gains.

Forskolin has been identified as the pharmacologically active principle in this plant, although its exact mode of action is unknown. It is understood to stimulate cellular adenylate cyclase and increase the production of cyclic AMP (3',5'-adenosine monophosphate), a secondary messenger involved in imparting many receptor-dependant functions.[237] This may allow forskolin to heighten cellular responsiveness to certain hormones and signaling ligands, many of which have activities integral to the metabolism and utilization of proteins, fats, and carbohydrates. Forskolin is also believed to exert a number of non-cyclic-AMP dependent activities, although the exact nature of these pathways is less understood.[238]

Sport supplement extracts of coleus forskohlii are typically standardized for forskolin content. They can vary significantly with regard to percentage of active forskolin, likely due to different plant origins and extraction methods. While clinical studies do suggest that forskolin can increase cyclic-AMP, the biological value of this (in the context of performance enhancement) remains unknown. Data confirming clear ergogenic value in experienced exercising adults is presently lacking.

Promoted Benefits:

Coleus forskohlii extract is promoted to increase testosterone levels, facilitating gains in lean muscle mass and strength.

Clinical Studies:

Coleus forskohlii extract has been shown to improve a metabolic marker (testosterone levels) often linked to positive changes in body composition or performance in human placebo-controlled studies . It has a Clinical Support Rating of 3 (3/5).

The most widely referenced and relevant placebo-controlled study of coleus forskohlii extract involved its supplementation by a group of inactive (sedentary) overweight men.[239] Subjects consumed 500 mg of extract per day (standardized for 10% forskolin) for a period of 12 weeks. There was no exercise as part of this study. The supplementation of coleus forskohlii extract resulted in a very slight but statistically significant increase in serum free testosterone levels (+3.47%) compared to placebo (-4.11%). There was also a statistically strong trend toward increased total testosterone (+16.77% versus -1.08%) and lean body mass gains (+3.71 kg versus +1.57 kg). The most notable change reported in this study was actually a reduction in fat mass (-4% versus -1%).

The positive hormonal adaptations subsequent to coleus forskohlii extract use were minor, and are of unknown value to sports performance. Further research is needed to determine if coleus forskohlii extract can provide ergogenic value to healthy exercising adults.

Empirical Evidence:
Coleus forskohlii extract is widely available as a stand-alone nutritional supplement. The feedback on its use as a sport supplement has been very mixed. Some users do claim to notice positive changes, usually with regard to body composition (lean mass) over time. Some also concurrently report improvements in muscle endurance and strength. An equally strong percentage of users, however, fail to notice any performance or body composition benefit from taking this supplement. Whether this inconsistency is the result of individual variances in sensitivity to coleus forskohlii extract, the context of its use, or a complete lack of ergogenic efficacy remains unclear. Coleus forskohlii extract has an Empirical Evidence Rating of 3 (3/5).

Effective Dosage:
An effective dosage of this supplement is unknown. Based on clinical studies showing minor testosterone elevations, a dosage of 50 mg per day (active forskolin) is commonly used.

Side Effects / Safety:
Coleus forskohlii extract was well tolerated during clinical studies, with no significant side effects. Mild gastrointestinal side effects (nausea, diarrhea etc.) are sometimes noted when initiating use or taking higher doses.

Conjugated-Linoleic Acid (CLA)

syn. c9,t11-CLA and t10,c12-CLA

PERFORMANCE VALIDATION SCORES	
Combined	8
Clinical Support Rating	4
Empirical Evidence Rating	4

Description:

Conjugated-linoleic acid (CLA) refers to a mixture of two or more double-bond isomers of the Omega-6 essential fatty acid linoleic acid. Common dietary sources of CLA include dairy products and meat.[240] Conjugated-linoleic acid is considered to be both a cis and trans fatty acid, though it is not counted as a trans fat on nutrition labels, nor believed to have the same deleterious effects on metabolism.[241] While conjugated-linoleic acid is not considered an essential nutrient in the diet, it does appear to exert biological activity in humans. It is widely used in supplement form as an antioxidant, to support general health, and lower serum lipids.[242] Principle to its use in sports nutrition, CLA is believed to exert positive effects on body composition under some conditions of use.

Studies suggest conjugated-linoleic acid has several potential health-protecting activities in the body.[243] To begin with, it appears to have strong antioxidant properties, which are mediated (at least in part) via increases in the antioxidant enzymes catalase and glutathione peroxidase. CLA may also exert anti-can-cer (tumor regressing) properties. Although its exact mode of action here is still the subject of much study, it has been shown to up-regulate a tumor-suppressing gene known as PTPRG (protein tyrosine phosphatase, receptor type, G). CLA also has been shown to lower levels of interleukins IL-6 and IL-1, which are mediators of inflammation. This may result in an anti-in-flammatory effect. This nutrient may also improve peripheral insulin sensitivity,[244] and increase bone mineral density.[245]

Conjugated-linoleic acid may also have positive effects on fat and energy metabolism.[246] This may be mediated in part via increases in acyl-CoA oxidase, which is an enzyme involved in fatty acid oxidation, polyunsaturated fatty acid synthesis, and increased PPAR (peroxisome proliferator-activated receptors) signaling.[247] CLA may also increase uncoupling protein-2 (UCP-2) mRNA expression, which is a protein found largely in skeletal muscle tissue, and involved in mitochondrial energy production. Some studies with animals suggest the supplementation of CLA can lower body fat levels and increase lean body mass.[248,249] Human studies with sedentary subjects do appear to support such activities, although conclusive ergogenic effects in training-experienced individuals have not yet been demonstrated.

It is of note that the effects of conjugated-linoleic acid appear to be isomer dependant.[250,251] The two most abundant isomers in CLA have been identified as c9,t11-CLA and t10,c12-CLA. In some cases, the isomers may have conflicting effects. For example, studies suggest that the t10,c12-CLA isomer is responsible for increasing fat oxidation and lean mass retention, but also contributes to insulin resistance.[252] One the other hand, the c9,t11-CLA isomer appears to reduce insulin resistance. Commercial CLA supplements, and often those used in studies showing positive metabolic benefits, tend to contain a balanced mixture of these two isomers.

Promoted Benefits:
Conjugated-linoleic acid is promoted to increase lean muscle mass and reduce body fat retention.

Clinical Studies:
This ingredient has been shown to improve body composition and gender specific performance in placebo-controlled studies with untrained adults. It has a Clinical Support Rating of 4 (4/5).

One placebo-controlled study examined the effects of conjugated-linoleic acid supplementation on body composition, strength, and markers of muscle degradation in a group of sedentary (inactive) men and women.[253] Subjects took 5 grams of CLA per day for a period of seven weeks, and followed a controlled resistance-training program. The use of CLA was shown to produce a slight but statistically significant increase in lean body mass compared to placebo (+1.4 kg versus +.2 kg). There was also a greater loss of fat mass (-.8 kg versus +.4 kg). Additionally, male subjects taking CLA noticed a greater increase in bench press strength than those taking placebo. The use of CLA was also associated with a lower catabolic effect of training, as measured by 3-methylhistidine (a marker of muscle fiber breakdown).

A second placebo-controlled study examined the effects of CLA on body composition, strength, and markers of catabolism in a group of experienced resistance-trained male athletes.[254] Subjects consumed 6 grams of CLA per day for four weeks, during which time they continued a resistance-training program. The supplementation of conjugated-linoleic acid was not shown to produce any statistically significant changes in performance, fat or lean mass, or markers of muscle breakdown compared to placebo. There were some statistically strong trends of improvement, however, suggesting that CLA may have exerted some ergogenic effect in a majority of subjects. It remains unknown if a higher dosage, longer period of intake, or different methodologies would have yielded statistically significant results.

Some other studies have failed to report statistically significant or statistically strong findings. While conflicting, the data on CLA does support ergogenic action. Further research is needed, however, to determine if conjugated-linoleic acid exhibits consistent performance-enhancing properties in exercise-experienced adults.

Empirical Evidence:
Conjugated-linoleic acid is widely available as a stand-alone nutritional supplement. The feedback on its use as a sport supplement tends to be positive. Most reports support its ability to reduce fat mass retention. For this purpose, bodybuilders commonly use CLA during bulking phases of training in an effort to better partition nutrients towards the gain of lean mass, or at least to limit the retention of fat when increasing calories. Less common are reports of significant muscle gain, strength increases, or improved exercise or sports performance as a result of CLA supplementation. A minority of users fail to notice any body composition or performance benefits with the use of this supplement. Whether this is due to an individual insensitivity to CLA, or particular instances in which it can impart positive metabolic effects, remains unknown. Conjugated-linoleic acid has an Empirical Evidence Rating of 4 (4/5).

Effective Dosage:

Based on clinical studies, a dosage of 5-6 grams per day (mixed isomers) is recommended.

Side Effects / Safety:

Conjugated-linoleic acid was well tolerated during clinical studies, with no health-significant side effects reported. A small percentage of users appear to notice minor gastrointestinal disturbance (upset stomach, diarrhea).[255]

Creatine

syn. alpha-methyl guandino-acetic acid
syn. creatine (various salts and derivatives)

PERFORMANCE VALIDATION SCORES	
Combined	10
Clinical Support Rating	5
Empirical Evidence Rating	5

Description:

Creatine is an amino acid derivative that is synthesized in the body from arginine, glycine, and methionine, mainly in the liver and kidneys. Approximately 95% of the creatine found in the body is stored in skeletal muscle tissue.[256] The body manufacturers approximately 1 gram of creatine per day, and the average person (with an omnivorous diet) ingests another 1 gram from meat and fish. Although not considered an essential part of the diet due to endogenous manufacture, creatine remains an extremely important biological component. It is integrally involved in energy metabolism in the muscles, the protein (nitrogen) balance, and cell membrane stability. It is also one of the most widely used sport supplement products, and is commonly applied to help increase muscle size, strength, and exercise performance.

Creatine supports the resynthesis of ATP (adenosine triphosphate) during anaerobic exercise, which is the primary carrier of cellular energy.[257] In a reversible reaction, creatine borrows a phosphate group from ATP to form phosphocreatine and ADP (adenosine diphosphate). When energy is needed, this phosphocreatine will return the borrowed phosphate to ADP, again yielding ATP. This is a constant cyclic process, which allows the muscles to rapidly expend and replenish energy. The phosphocreatine-ATP cycle sustains maximum energy output for only a brief period of time, however. During high intensity output, the ATP resynthesis rate quickly fails to keep up with utilization, resulting in muscle fatigue. The normal biological turnover of creatine is about 2 grams per day.[258] Supplementation beyond this level raises tissue creatine/phosphocreatine concentrations, enhancing ATP energy output during anaerobic exercise.

An increase in the content of creatine inside the muscle cell also produces a shift in the osmotic balance. This causes a phenomenon known as water drag, where the muscle cell pulls in water from the surrounding environment to reestablish osmotic balance. This hydration effect causes an increase in total body water retention. This typically accounts for 2-5 lbs of weight gain within the first week of initiating creatine supplementation.[259] This tends to produce a visible increase in the overall size of the muscles, indistinguishable from increases due to protein retention. Since this water tends to be retained in the intracellular compartment, creatine supplementation is usually not associated with visible bloating and loss of definition.[260]

While cell hydration may account for much of the initial size increase due to creatine supplementation, its continued use also tends to produce significant muscle cell hypertrophy. Its exact mechanism of action here, however, it not fully understood. Studies examining amino acid kinetics during creatine supplementation have demonstrated a decrease in muscle protein breakdown during exercise (an anti-catabolic effect).[261] Creatine also supports the increased expression of IGF-1 in the muscles, a key anabolic hormone.[262,263] Studies also show that creatine can increase the expression of myogenin and MRF-4.[264] These two transcriptional factors support myosin heavy chain synthesis, which is the main contractile protein in muscle. Creatine also appears to support the satellite cell cycle, which helps expand the functional size capacity of the muscle cell.[265]

The body has a threshold for maximum creatine retention in skeletal muscle.[266] The saturation point (depending on diet) is usually between 10-40% above normal levels.[267] Vegetarians consume less creatine, and tend to have lower levels. Once reaching the saturation point, there is no added benefit to consuming higher doses. The extra will simply be excreted in the urine. The use of a daily dose of 20 grams of creatine (monohydrate) will result in tissue saturation after as little as two to three days. After this point, lower doses will maintain elevated tissues stores. The common recommendation is for a brief loading period of 20 grams daily for five days, followed by maintenance dose of 3-5 grams per day until the end of use.[268] One can alternately use as little as 3 grams per day (no loading period), but it can take up to 30 days to achieve tissue saturation.[269]

As a nutritional supplement, creatine is available in many different salts and ester forms including creatine monohydrate, ethyl ester, citrate, tricreatine citrate, pyruvate, and magnesium-creatine chelate. Creatine monohydrate is the most common, and also (by far) the most widely investigated and proven in a clinical setting. All creatine products are intended to increase the content of creatine and phosphocreatine in the muscles. This is important to remember. While the various forms may differ slightly from one another with regard to solubility properties, rate of digestion, and free creatine yield per gram, all are subject to the same limits of tissue creatine saturation. Also, bioavailability improvements over creatine monohydrate are unlikely since monohydrate is already estimated to exhibit near 100% absorption from the gastrointestinal tract.[270]

Creatine Yield (per 5 grams)	
5 g	creatine (pure)
4.4 g	creatine monohydrate
3.4 g	creatine ethyl ester HCL
3.36 g	tricreatine citrate
3 g	creatine pyruvate
2.27 g	magnesium creatine chelate
2 g	creatine citrate

Creatine is the most widely used ergogenic substance in the world. It is also the most extensively investigated, and has been the subject of more than 100 clinical studies. The results of these studies show that the short-term supplementation can effectively raise the content of creatine in the muscles. This shifts the osmotic balance, resulting in water influx and cell expansion. This also increases the cellular reserves of creatine and phosphocreatine, which support anaerobic energy metabolism. Creatine supplementation also tends to support a positive protein balance over time. Creatine is an effective sport supplement for weightlifting, and other activities where brief repeat bursts of energy are required such as sprinting, jumping, football, soccer, and baseball.[271]

Promoted Benefits:

Creatine is promoted to increase muscle creatine and phosphocreatine stores, support increased muscle mass and strength, and enhance energy and performance during anaerobic exercise.

Clinical Studies:

Creatine has been the subject of extensive clinical study. This ingredient has been shown to improve body composition and performance in placebo-controlled studies with trained adults. Its Clinical Support Rating is 5 (5/5).

creatine monohydrate

One of the most widely referenced placebo-controlled studies examined the effects of creatine monohydrate supplementation on resistance training performance in a group of experienced weightlifting men.[272] Each subject ingested a loading dose of 25 grams per day for one week, followed by a maintenance dose of 5 grams daily for the remainder of the experiment. The supplementation continued for 12 weeks, during which time all participants underwent a heavy resistance-training program. The supplementation of creatine resulted in a statistically significant increase in lean body mass (6.3% versus 3.1%) compared to placebo. Creatine monohydrate also resulted in greater increases in bench press (24% versus 16%) and squat strength (32% versus 24%) compared to placebo. An examination of muscle fiber content showed that subjects taking creatine monohydrate had significantly greater increases in all three fiber types compared to placebo: Type I (35% versus 11%), Type IIA (36% versus 15%), and Type IIAB (35% versus 6%). Training volume was also increased in the creatine monohydrate group.

Another placebo-controlled study examined the effects of creatine monohydrate supplementation on both muscle and aerobic performance in a group of competitive rugby players.[273] One focus of this study was to see if an increase in muscle mass would hinder aerobic performance. The subjects ingested .1 grams of creatine monohydrate per kg of bodyweight per day, for a total period of eight weeks. This equates to a dose of 7 grams per day for a person of 70 kg (154 lbs). During the experiment, players followed their normal training and game schedules. Measures of body composition, muscle endurance (number of repetitions at 75% 1-rep maximum in bench and leg press), and aerobic endurance (shuttle-run test with progressively increasing speed) were taken before and after eight weeks of supplementation. Subjects taking creatine monohydrate noticed a statistically significant improvement in muscle endurance (+5.8 versus +0.9 repetitions) compared to placebo. There was no change in aerobic endurance. While not statistically significant, there was also a trend toward increased lean mass (+1.2 kg) in subjects taking creatine monohydrate.

In addition to the above, there are many other placebo-controlled studies examining the effects of creatine monohydrate under anaerobic exercise conditions. Some of these investigations have failed to note statistically significant improvements in certain measures of performance and/or body composition.[274, 275, 276] This likely reflects methodological difficulties due to many other confounding variables such as diet, exercise, training experience, and individual genetic factors. The ergogenic properties of creatine with anaerobic exercise are widely accepted as valid. Creatine monohydrate supplementation does not appear to strongly influence oxygen consumption or performance in aerobic activities (such as long distance running).[277]

creatine ethyl ester

In one placebo-controlled study, the effect of creatine ethyl ester on body composition and exercise performance was compared to an equal dose of creatine monohydrate in a group of healthy men.[278] Subjects consumed 20 grams of either form of creatine each day for five days (loading), followed by 5 grams daily for the remaining six weeks. All participants followed a controlled heavy resistance-training program. Creatine ethyl ester was shown to be not as effective as monohydrate at raising serum and muscle creatine content, nor at supporting increases in lean body mass, strength, or muscle power. While exercise improvements were made in the ethyl ester group, it was not possible to attribute them to supplementation.

The above study did suggest that creatine ethyl ester was much less stable than monohydrate, as serum levels of the main creatine metabolite (creatinine) were significantly higher in comparison. This is in agreement with another incubation study that suggests creatine ethyl ester has a half-life in human serum of only about one minute, which may be too short to reach muscle tissue in significant levels.[279] Further research on creatine ethyl ester is needed.

creatine citrate

One placebo-controlled study examined the effects of five weeks of creatine citrate supplementation on handgrip exercise performance in a group of healthy men.[280] Subjects consumed 5 grams of creatine citrate per day, which is equivalent to 3 grams of base creatine. Subjects taking creatine citrate noticed statistically significant improvements in mean power and contraction velocity compared to placebo. These results suggest that creatine citrate possesses similar ergogenic activity as creatine monohydrate, although no direct comparison between the two has been made.

tricreatine citrate

In pharmacokinetic studies, tricreatine citrate was shown to produce a similar increase in the serum creatine level compared to creatine monohydrate (when taken in base-creatine equivalent doses).[281] This study suggests that tricreatine citrate possesses similar ergogenic activity as creatine monohydrate.

creatine pyruvate

The effects of five weeks of creatine pyruvate supplementation on handgrip exercise performance were compared to an equal dose of creatine citrate in a placebo-controlled study with healthy men.[282] Subjects consumed 5 grams of either creatine per day, equivalent to 3 grams of base creatine. Both groups noticed statistically significant improvements in mean power and contraction velocity compared to placebo. Creatine pyruvate also produced improvements in relaxation velocity and oxygen consumption not noted with creatine citrate.

Another study examined the effects of creatine pyruvate on exercise performance in a group of Olympic canoeists.[283] Each subject ingested 7.5 grams of creatine pyruvate daily for five days, which is equivalent to about 5 grams of creatine monohydrate (base creatine content). The supplementation of creatine pyruvate resulted in improvements in paddling speed and serum lactate buildup (reduced), suggesting improvements in aerobic metabolism.

A pharmacokinetic study demonstrated that creatine pyruvate was 17% and 14% more effective at raising serum creatine levels compared to tricreatine citrate and creatine monohydrate, respectively.[284] The creatines were administered at base-creatine equivalent doses, which amounted to 7.3 g of creatine pyruvate, 6.7 g of tricreatine citrate, and 5 g of creatine monohydrate.

magnesium-creatine chelate

One placebo-controlled study examined the effects of magnesium-creatine chelate on exercise performance in a group of healthy subjects.[285] Each participant took a dose equivalent to 800 mg of magnesium and 5 grams of creatine per day for a period of two weeks. Subjects taking magnesium-creatine chelate noticed statistically significant improvements in muscle torque and total body water (intracellular compartment), which were better than subjects taking creatine monohydrate plus a seperate magnesium oxide supplement. Other studies suggest that magnesium-creatine chelate possesses similar ergogenic activity to creatine monohydrate.[286]

Empirical Evidence:

Creatine is widely available as a stand-alone nutritional supplement. The feedback on its use as a sport supplement has been strongly positive. Creatine is, in fact, one of the most reliable ergogenic supplements in common use today. Most users report a rapid increase in bodyweight (up to five pounds) within the first week of use at tissue saturation levels. The continued use of this supplement for six to eight weeks tends to also lead to a substantial increase in muscle protein content, often amounting to another 5 lbs or more of weight gain. This supplement also seems highly valued in a wide variety of competitive sports where intermitted bouts of high intensity exertion are required. A small percentage of users appear to be non-responsive to creatine use. This seems to be in agreement with studies suggesting that a minority of users (20-30%) are unable to appreciably saturate tissues with creatine, even after loading phases of use, due to some unknown variable.[287] Creatine has an Empirical Evidence Rating of 5 (5/5).

Effective Dosage:

Based on clinical studies, a loading phase of 20 g daily (creatine monohydrate) is recommended for 5 days at the start of use, which is followed by a maintenance dosage of 3-5 grams per day until the end of supplementation. The consumption of simple carbohydrates with creatine monohydrate has been shown to increase tissue creatine stores by an additional 9% over the use of creatine alone.[288] To maintain maximum effectiveness, creatine is typically taken for a period of 6-12 weeks, followed by an equal amount of time off. Creatine levels may stay elevated for up to six weeks after stopping supplementation.[289]

Side Effects / Safety:

Creatine supplementation appears to be safe in healthy individuals. One long-term study examined the use of 4 grams of creatine monohydrate daily for two years in elderly patients with Parkinson disease.[290] The supplementation of creatine was well tolerated, and failed to produce health significant side effects. A small number of subjects reported minor gastrointestinal disturbances, but there were no negative changes in any marker of general or renal health. Note that creatine breaks down to creatinin, which can interfere with diagnostic tests of kidney function. Creatine supplementation according to common guidelines is not believed to harm healthy kidney function.

Dehydroepiandrosterone (DHEA)

syn. 3beta-hydroxy-5-androsten-17-one
syn. prasterone

PERFORMANCE VALIDATION SCORES	
Combined	6
Clinical Support Rating	4
Empirical Evidence Rating	2

Description:

Dehydroepiandrosterone (DHEA) is a steroid hormone produced mainly in the adrenal glands. It is one of the most abundant steroid hormones in humans, although its exact biological role remains unclear. DHEA is known to serve as an indirect precursor to many sex steroids, including estrogen and testosterone.[291] DHEA itself has also been shown to be a weak androgen,[292] although in a practical sense it is considered to be devoid of significant anabolic or androgenic activity. It is believed to have some supportive action in the immune system, potentially countering the suppressive effects of the stress hormone cortisol.[293] DHEA is also regarded as an active component in the central nervous systems,[294] may be involved in IGF-1 synthesis,[295] and appears to have some cortisol inhibiting (protein sparing) effect.[296]

The level of dehydroepiandrosterone in the blood tends to get lower with age, and is especially low in the elderly.[297,298] This DHEA reduction mirrors the age related decline in testosterone synthesis. When associated with physical symptoms, this testosterone decline is medically identified as andropause, and often treated with supplemental testosterone. Given the potential precursor relationship to testosterone (as well as the natural lowering of DHEA), dehydroepiandrosterone has been widely sold as a non-prescription anti-aging and hormone replacement supplement for men and women. Its exact therapeutic value in this context, however, remains unclear.[299,300] DHEA is also widely available as a sports nutrition product due to its theoretical potential for increasing the muscle-building effects of testosterone.

DHEA is two steps away (metabolically) from testosterone. It must first be converted to either androstenedione or androstenediol. This indirect conversion makes DHEA a very ineffective oral testosterone precursor. It appears that this hormone does not significantly contribute to the synthesis of testosterone in men. Even high doses (1,600 mg) have been shown to be ineffective at raising blood testosterone levels.[301] Thus far, significant testosterone elevations have been reported in postmenopausal women only.[302,303] Men tend to notice only minor shifts in estrogen and IGF-1. Studies do suggest there is potential for DHEA to improve exercise performance in the elderly of both sexes, possibly through testosterone-independent mechanisms.[304] It appears unlikely, however, that DHEA supplementation will have testosterone-elevating or ergogenic effects in healthy exercising young men.

Promoted Benefits:
DHEA is promoted to increase testosterone levels, and support muscle mass and strength gains.

Clinical Studies:
DHEA has been shown to improve body composition in placebo-controlled studies with sedentary (untrained) adults. It has a Clinical Support Rating of 4 (4/5).

One placebo-controlled study examined the effects of high doses of DHEA on body composition and hormone levels in a group of healthy men.[305] Subjects took 1,600 mg of DHEA per day for four weeks. There was no exercise as part of this study. The use of DHEA was associated with a 31% reduction in fat mass, with no change in total body weight. This suggests the weight loss was associated with an increase in skeletal muscle mass. In spite of this high dose, there was no change in total testosterone, free testosterone, or estrogen levels.

Another placebo-controlled study examined the effects of long-term DHEA supplementation on exercise performance in elderly subjects.[306] The dosage used was 50 mg per day, which was taken for 10 months. During the last four months all participants were subject to a controlled heavy resistance-training program. The subjects taking DHEA noticed greater improvements in muscle strength (knee extension torque and knee flexion torque) compared to those taking the placebo. Testosterone levels increased significantly (300%) only in female subjects taking DHEA. Estrogen levels increased 30% and 70% in supplemented men and women, respectively. Levels of IGF-1 (Insulin-like Growth Factor 1) also increased slightly in both men and women taking DHEA.

Studies with younger populations taking DHEA as an adjunct to exercise have not yielded the same positive results. For example, one placebo-controlled study examined the effects of DHEA on exercise performance in a group of young men.[307] Subjects took a dose of 150 mg per day for eight weeks, during which time they followed a controlled resistance-training program. The use of DHEA did not produce statistically significant improvements in testosterone levels, muscle strength, or lean body mass compared to placebo.

Another placebo-controlled study looked at the effects of dehydroepiandrosterone in a group of healthy trained (> 1 year experience) men.[308] Subjects took 100 mg per day for a period of 12 weeks. The use of DHEA did not produce a statistically significant increase in serum testosterone levels, lean body mass, or exercise performance (muscle strength) compared to placebo.

While these studies do not support the use of DHEA as an ergogenic aid in young exercising populations, they do suggest the supplement might improve body composition and exercise performance in elderly men and women.

Empirical Evidence:
DHEA is widely available as a stand-alone supplement. The feedback on its use in sports nutrition tends to be negative. To begin with, men who use this product as a testosterone booster in the hopes it will increase muscle mass and strength generally wind up disappointed. It is rare to find reports of noticeable anabolic or androgenic effects from young men taking DHEA. This seems in line with clinical studies showing that DHEA is not effective at raising testosterone levels or improving exercise performance in young men. However, this supplement does appear to offer some ergogenic value in women, as well as the elderly of both sexes. Were we focusing on vitality

and "anti-aging" use in older people, DHEA would warrant a strong empirical evidence rating (4/5), as it is often very highly regarded amongst these consumers. As it stands for our purposes, DHEA receives an overall Empirical Evidence Rating of 2 (2/5), given its weak application as an ergogen in sports nutrition.

Effective Dosage:

Based on clinical studies, a dosage of 50-200 mg per day is recommended in elderly exercising men and women. An effective dosage in young exercising individuals has not been established.

Side Effects / Safety:

DHEA was well tolerated during clinical studies, with no significant side effects reported.

Ecdysterone

syn. 20-hydroxyecdysone
syn. isoinokosterone

Description:

Ecdysterone (20-hydroxyecdysone) is a steroid hormone involved in development and reproductive function in arthropods, a category of invertebrates. It is most widely identified as an insect hormone, where it plays a prominent role in molting (the technical term for molting is ecdysis). Ecdysterone belongs to a large family of related chemicals known as ecdysteroids. These compounds are structurally distinct from human steroid hormones, and are not known to bind the human androgen receptor. Ecdysteroids are also found in many plant species (phytoecdysteroids), presumably as part of an evolved defense mechanism that disrupts the reproductive system of pest insects. Plant extracts are the primary source for supplemental ecdysteroids, although synthetic manufacturing techniques are also known.

Although ecdysterone is an invertebrate hormone, it has been shown to exhibit some biological activity in mammals. The exact nature of this activity, however, remains unclear. Animal studies have demonstrated a diverse set of potential properties.[309] This includes the support of reproductive functioning, nervous system functioning, heart and circulatory health, liver detoxification, immunity, and kidney function. Ecdysterone also appears to have some influence over cell proliferation, as well as protein, carbohydrate, and lipid metabolism. When noted, the associated changes in metabolism are generally positive, such as a lowering of blood sugar, increased synthesis of protein, and a reduction in serum cholesterol.

While ecdysterone has been the subject of animal investigations for more than 40 years, the therapeutic value of this substance in humans remains unknown. Since this hormone is known to have some biological activity in humans, it would not be surprising to see some medical applications further substantiated. Progress in this area, however, has been surprisingly slow. There is much speculation that the growth promoting effects of this compound in animals may also translate into increased exercise performance in humans, perhaps even leading to greater gains in muscle mass and strength. Presently, however, there are no peer-reviewed studies conclusively demonstrating such activity.

Promoted Benefits:

Ecdysterone is promoted to help increase muscle mass, strength, and anaerobic endurance.

Clinical Studies:

The use of ecdysterone as a sport supplement is sup

ported by animal data only. Its Clinical Support Rating is 2 (2/5).

Ecdysterone has been the subject of many studies, particularly in Eastern Europe. Positive changes have been reported in a number of animal experiments, which might translate to exercise performance benefits in humans. For example, one set of studies demonstrated that untrained rats given ecdysterone for 20 days had more exercise endurance than unsupplemented animals.[310] Another study showed increased muscle adenosine triphosphate levels (a form of stored energy) in vitamin D deficient rats given ecdysterone.[311] Other studies have shown increased bodyweight in pigs[312] and quails[313] fed diets enriched with this phytoecdysteroid.

Sport supplement manufacturers commonly reference three additional Russian studies on ecdysterone. One study demonstrated a 6-7% improvement in lean body mass, and a 10% reduction in body fat, in a group of 78 highly trained athletes given ecdysterone.[314] This was reported after only 10 days of supplementation. The second study demonstrated increased lean muscle mass, decreased body fat, and increased muscle endurance in exercising adults following 21 days of use.[315] The third found ecdysterone more effective at increasing muscle endurance, and possessing a wider spectrum of anabolic action, than the steroid Dianabol.[316] While these results are all extremely compelling, they were published in obscure Russian journals, usually with incomplete methodological details. This has made objective evaluation very difficult. Some of the improvements are also so remarkable as to question their validity. These studies are generally not accepted as credible evaluations of ecdysterone by Western academics.

There has been only one placebo-controlled study published in a reputable Western peer-reviewed journal that examines the effects of ecdysterone supple-

mentation on exercising adults.[317] The study involved the supplementation of ecdysterone for eight weeks (30 mg/day) in a group of men with resistance-training experience. A detailed resistance-training program was followed as part of the study, and measurements of strength and anaerobic performance were taken at various points throughout the experiment. Investigators could find no statistically significant or strong trends of improvement in any marker of exercise performance, anabolic/catabolic status, or body composition as a result of ecdysterone supplementation. This study does not support the use of ecdysterone to enhance exercise or athletic performance.

Empirical Evidence:
Ecdysterone has been widely used as a stand-alone product. The empirical evidence on this supplement has been only weakly positive. It appears that a majority of users fail to notice any significant benefit from this supplement. It is common to hear someone convey the belief that this compound is completely without merit as a sports nutrition product. At the same time, however, you can find some support for its use. A fair percentage of users do claim to notice some type of positive results from ecdysterone supplementation. Some even become loyal repeat users of these products. There is enough disparity in perceived results that two distinct camps seem to have formed over the value (or not) of this compound to athletes. Ecdysterone has an Empirical Evidence Rating of 2 (2/5).

Effective Dosage:
An effective dosage of this supplement has not been established. Manufacturers commonly recommend 30-60 mg of ecdysterone per day.

Side Effects / Safety:
Ecdysterone does not appear to have toxic effects in humans.[318]

Fenugreek Extract

syn. 4-hydroxyisoleucine
syn. Trigonella foenum-graecum

PERFORMANCE VALIDATION SCORES	
Combined	6
Clinical Support Rating	3
Empirical Evidence Rating	3

Description:

Fenugreek is a medicinal plant originally of Indian and North African origin. It has been an integral part of Ayurvedic and Chinese traditional medicine for ages, used for such things as the treatment of indigestion, baldness, edema of the legs, the induction of labor, and the stimulation of lactation.[319] It has also been widely used as a tonic, to increase metabolism, energy, and a sense of wellbeing. Additionally, Fenugreek has been applied to help increase the appetite and promote weight gain.[320] More recently, Fenugreek, specifically extract of the seeds, has been sold as a sport supplement for increasing testosterone levels and improving exercise performance.

The most pronounced activity of fenugreek seed extract seems to be a strong hypoglycemic effect. Clinical research suggests that it lowers blood sugar through several distinct mechanisms. For one, the seed extract contains high levels of an amino acid called 4-hydroxyisoleucine. This amino acid helps stimulate the release of insulin from the pancreas in response to serum glucose (blood sugar).[321] Fenugreek also seems to increase the number of insulin receptors in various tissues, increasing hormone sensitivity.[322] It also appears to inhibit intestinal enzymes involved in the breakdown of sugars and starch.[323] Together, these factors may allow this extract to be an effective supportive treatment in type-2 diabetic patients, helping to regulate both resting glucose levels and the insulin response after meals.[324]

Fenugreek also appears to exhibit a measurable anti-hyperlipidemic effect,[325] which means that it might improve lipids in patients suffering from high cholesterol. It has specifically been shown in studies to lower total and LDL (bad) cholesterol levels, an activity that should create an environment more favorable (less atherogenic) for the cardiovascular system. This biological activity may be due in part to other components of Fenugreek seeds called sapogenins, which are known to increase the excretion of cholesterol in the bile. Fenugreek's cholesterol lowering effect may also be due in part to another compound called disogenin, which has some estrogenic activity.[326] Some components of the fenugreek seed have also been shown to stimulate the release of growth hormone in rats.[327] Additional human studies are necessary to determine if fenugreek seed extract can improve human exercise performance.

Promoted Benefits:

Fenugreek seed extract is promoted to elevate testosterone, increase glycogen storage, and improve muscle mass and athletic performance.

Clinical Studies:

This ingredient has been shown in human placebo-controlled studies to improve a metabolic marker (glycogen synthesis) often linked to positive changes in body composition or performance. It has a Clinical Support Rating of 3 (3/5).

One study examined the addition of hydroxy-isoleucine (extracted from Fenugreek seeds) to a post-exercise carbohydrate drink high in dextrose.[328] The amount of 4-hydroxyisoleucine used was 2 mg/kg of bodyweight. Each of the study participants was subject to 90 minutes of intense exercise, which was aimed at depleting muscle glycogen stores. A baseline measure of the muscle tissue glycogen level was taken immediately after exercise. This was compared to samples following carbohydrate replenishment during a 4-hour recovery window. The study demonstrated that the addition of 4-hydroxyisoleucine from fenugreek seeds improved glycogen resynthesis rates by 63% over the consumption of carbohydrates alone.

Another study on mice examined the effect of fenugreek seed extract on endurance exercise performance.[329] Four weeks of fenugreek supplementation resulted in a significant increase in the time to exhaustion during prolonged swimming exercise. Body fat levels also decreased significantly in the supplemented animals. Blood sample analysis demonstrated a concurrent rise in blood non-esterified fatty acid levels, suggesting an increase in the utilization of fat for energy.

Presently, there are no known published peer-reviewed clinical studies supporting the use of fenugreek seed extract for increasing testosterone levels in humans. Further research is needed to determine if fenugreek has a strong performance-enhancing effect in exercising adults.

Empirical Evidence:

Fenugreek seed extract has been widely used as a stand-alone product. The empirical evidence on this supplement has been very mixed. A good percentage of users do believe they notice some benefit from this supplement, usually with regard to an increase in muscle endurance. At the same time, an equally strong percentage of users cannot attribute positive results to the use of this supplement. It is possible that the ergogenic value of this supplement is isolated to its effect on insulin and glycogen resynthesis rates (presently the only action supported by placebo-controlled studies). In this case, the physiological changes may be too minor for many individuals to notice, especially if they are not closely in-tuned with their threshold for glycogen depletion. Fenugreek has an Empirical Evidence Rating of 3 (3/5).

Effective Dosage:

Based on clinical studies and empirical evidence, a dosage of 1-3 grams per day of fenugreek extract, or 2 mg/kg of 4-hydroxyisoleucine, is recommended.

Side Effects / Safety:

Fenugreek seed extract has been well tolerated during clinical studies, with few significant side effects. Note that fenugreek can lower blood sugar and cause a state of hypoglycemia. Care should be taken to assure sufficient carbohydrates are taken to maintain optimal blood glucose levels. Other common side effects include diarrhea and flatulence. Fenugreek also contains coumarin derivatives, which may increase bleeding time. Fenugreek should never be used during pregnancy due to its hormonal/uterine stimulating properties. Note that many bodybuilders and athletes prefer the use of purified 4-hydroxyisoleucine, and report fewer side effects compared to fenugreek seed extract. Studies comparing the safety of the two have not been conducted.

Fish Oil (EPA/DHA)

syn. eicosapentaenoic acid/docosahexaenoic acid

PERFORMANCE VALIDATION SCORES	
Combined	7
Clinical Support Rating	3
Empirical Evidence Rating	4

Description:

Fish oil supplements are generally provided as a rich source of the omega-3 polyunsaturated fatty acids eicosapentaenoic acid (EPA) and docosahexaenoic acid (DHA). Omega 3 fatty acids are important to human nutrition, and cannot be synthesized by the body. As such, they are regarded as essential dietary nutrients. The consumption of small amounts of these essential fatty acids is necessary for many biological functions including human growth and development, cell membrane functioning, nutrient metabolism, nervous system functioning, vision, memory, and cognition.[330,331,332] In sports nutrition, fish oil supplements are widely used for their potential benefits on metabolism and overall health.

Fish oil supplementation has several well-supported health-beneficial effects. To begin with, EPA/DHA have been shown to lower triglyceride levels.[333] In fact, there is a prescription drug form of EPA and DHA (Lovaza, GlaxoSmithKline) for treating high triglyceride levels. These fatty acids may also reduce serum cholesterol levels,[334] improve vascular reactivity[335] and endothelial function,[336] and have antiarrhythmic activities.[337] Studies show that regular supplementation of EPA and DHA helps protect the cardiovascular system, substantially reducing the risk of sudden cardiac death.[338,339] EPA and DHA have also been shown to possess anti-inflammatory activities,[340] and may help treat inflammatory diseases such as arthritis[341] and asthma.[342] Some studies also suggest EPA and DHA may improve mood and memory,[343]

and prevent protein catabolism in certain diseased states.[344,345]

Eicosapentaenoic acid and docosahexaenoic acid also have some effects on metabolism that may be of benefit to exercising individuals. For starters, omega-3 fatty acid supplementation inhibits several enzymes involved in lipogenesis (fat deposition).[346] They are also important to the oxidation of fatty acids for energy.[347] This may help improve body composition, at least by reducing fat retention. Omega-3 fatty acids may also increase the activity of antioxidant enzymes.[348] This can help to clear free radicals, which may damage cells and potentially even contribute to muscle fatigue. EPA and DHA also have vasodilatory effects,[349] which can increase blood flow and nutrient delivery to the muscles. They may also help maintain exercise functionality by reducing muscle soreness following intense training.[350]

Thus far, studies with exercising adults generally do not support direct ergogenic effects with fish oil supplementation. They do suggest, however, that EPA and DHA may improve cardiovascular fitness subsequent to exercise. This may allow the athlete to maintain a lower heart rate while performing endurance activities at near maximal oxygen consumption. The anti-inflammatory effects of EPA and DHA may also help protect against exercise-induced bronchoconstriction.[351] This sometimes occurs in elite and high-level non-asthmatic athletes, possibly due to the regular dehydration of the airways during intense exertion. Fish oil supplements do not appear to have muscle-building (anabolic) effects in healthy individuals.

Promoted Benefits:
Fish oil is promoted to improve body composition and exercise performance.

Clinical Studies:
Fish oil has been shown in human placebo-controlled studies to improve a metabolic marker (heart rate during endurance performance) linked to positive changes in performance. It has a Clinical Support Rating of 3 (3/5).

One placebo-controlled study examined the effects of fish oil on endurance exercise performance in a group of trained elite cyclists.[352] Subjects took 8 grams of fish oil per day for eight weeks. Each 1-gram fish oil capsule contained 325 mg of DHA and 65 mg of EPA. The use of fish oil did not produce positive changes in peak oxygen consumption, peak workload, ventilatory threshold, blood lactate concentrations, or time to fatigue compared to placebo in elite athletes. While there was no direct ergogenic effect noticed, subjects taking fish oil did maintain a lower heart rate during both incremental and endurance exercise, representing an improvement in cardiovascular fitness.

Another placebo-controlled study looked at the effects of 6 grams of fish oil per day during five weeks of exercise training in a group of Australian Rules football players.[353] The supplementation of fish oil again failed to produce a direct ergogenic effect as measured by time to exhaustion or recovery. It did, however, slightly lower blood pressure and improve cardiovascular fitness, as measured by a reduction in heart rate during submaximal exercise (-7.8 beats/min versus -1.9 beats/min) compared to placebo.

Consistent with the above two studies, a third placebo-controlled study also noticed improvements in cardiovascular fitness following the use of fish oil with exercise.[354] In this placebo-controlled study, well trained athletes (cyclists) took 8 grams of fish oil daily for eight weeks. The study found no differences in peak oxygen consumption (VO2peak), peak workload, or time to exhaustion after fish oil supplementation. Fish oil supplementation did, however, lower heart rate during incremental and steady submaximal exercise, and reduce whole-body oxygen consumption.

One uncontrolled study on the effects of fish oil supplementation in men with training experience suggests a more tangible ergogenic effect, but was far from conclusive.[355] As part of the investigation, each subject took 4 grams of fish oil daily for four weeks. Exercise performance was evaluated before and after with the use of treadmill running, first at 60% maximum oxygen consumption, followed by a high intensity incremental run until exhaustion. While fish oil failed to produce statistically significant improvements in any marker of exercise performance, there was a statistically strong trend of improvement in time to exhaustion pre- and post-supplementation (9.7 minutes versus 10.2 minutes).

Further research is needed to determine if fish oil supplementation can exhibit consistent performance-enhancing properties in exercising adults.

Empirical Evidence:
Fish oil (EPA/DHA) is widely available as a stand-alone nutritional supplement. The feedback on its use as a sport supplement tends to be positive. Fish oil is one of the most accepted general health supplements available, and is widely used by athletes and bodybuilders to improve cardiovascular fitness and protect wellness. The beneficial effects of fish oil on cardiovascular fitness sometimes translate into per-

formance improvements in athletes, particularly those competing in endurance-focused activities. Body-builders also sometimes favor fish oils for reducing body fat mass and improving muscle definition. While enough people do report tangible ergogenic effects with fish oil supplementation to consider this a positive trend, there is also a strong population of users discounting such activities. The reason for this discrepancy remains unclear, but may relate to particular sets of circumstances in which fish oil is able to impart beneficial effects on exercise performance. As an ergogenic aid, fish oil has an Empirical Evidence Rating of 4 (4/5).

Effective Dosage:

Based on clinical studies, a dosage of 3-6 grams of fish oil per day (standardized for EPA and DHA) is recommended.

Side Effects / Safety:

Fish oil is generally well tolerated, and considered to be a health-supportive supplement. Gastrointestinal side effects are sometimes reported, and in rare cases prolonged bleeding time of clinical significance has been reported as well.[356]

Gamma Oryzanol

syn. ferulic acid esters
syn. rice bran oil (extract)

PERFORMANCE VALIDATION SCORES	
Combined	**3**
Clinical Support Rating	2
Empirical Evidence Rating	1

Description:

Gamma oryzanol is a mixture of ferulic acid esters, sterols, and triterpene alcohols extracted from Japanese rice bran oil (oryza sativa). Ferulic acid is regarded as the primary active ingredient. Gamma oryzanol has been used as a natural remedy for decades, and appears to have a number of potential health promoting properties.[357] For one, it is a strong antioxidant. It also appears to be an effective natural treatment for high cholesterol. One study showed a 300 mg daily dosed significantly lowered total (204 to 176 mg/dL) and LDL (bad) cholesterol (124 to 101 mg/dL) levels in a group of men during 12 weeks of supplementation.[358] Gamma oryzanol may also protect against ulcers,[359] and alleviate certain symptoms of menopause.[360]

Gamma oryzanol supplements have been marketed to bodybuilders and athletes off and on for many years. The typical claim is that the products will increase anabolic (testosterone, growth hormone) levels, thereby supporting greater improvements in muscle size and strength. Unfortunately, there is little actual clinical or empirical data to support the use of gamma oryzanol in this manner. The one relevant independent clinical study with exercising adults reported no improvements in testosterone, growth hormone, or any marker of exercise performance with gamma oryzanol supplementation. Furthermore, some studies with animals suggest that ferulic acid may actually interfere with muscle gains and anabolic hormone levels.[361,362] Whether or not gamma oryzanol

has any value as a sport supplement remains to be seen.

Promoted Benefits:

Gamma oryzanol is promoted to increase testosterone and growth hormone levels, and support muscle mass and strength gains.

Clinical Studies:

The use of gamma oryzanol as a sport supplement is supported by animal data only. Its Clinical Support Rating is 2 (2/5).

The most commonly cited independent study demonstrating a positive effect on anabolic hormone levels involved the intravenous injection of ferulic acid (the principle active component of gamma oryzanol) in a group of cows.[363] The animals noticed a slight increase in growth hormone levels shortly after injection. This increase was short-lived, however, with levels returning to baseline approximately 60-90 minutes after administration.

There has been one independent placebo-controlled clinical study on the effects of gamma oryzanol supplementation by exercising adults.[364] It involved the use of 500 mg daily for a period of nine weeks. All subjects followed a controlled resistance-training program. The study reported no additional improvements in any measure of performance (bench press strength, squat strength, or vertical jump power) as a result of gamma oryzanol supplementation. Also, there were no differences in anabolic/catabolic hormone levels (testosterone, cortisol, growth hormone, or insulin) compared to those subjects taking placebo. This study does not support of the use gamma oryzanol as a sport supplement.

Further research is needed to determine if there is any ergogenic value to the use of gamma oryzanol by athletic individuals.

Empirical Evidence:
Gamma oryzanol has been widely used as a stand-alone supplement. The feedback on this supplement tends to be poor. A strong majority of people appear unable to attribute any specific benefit to gamma oryzanol with regard to muscle mass or strength increases. Most report the supplement to be ineffective. Only a small number of users seem to have positive experiences. Given the relatively low frequency of such reports, however, it is difficult to know if they are genuine, or the subject of placebo effect. Gamma oryzanol has an Empirical Evidence Rating of 1 (1/5).

Effective Dosage:
An effective dosage of this supplement has not been established. Manufacturers commonly recommend 300-500 mg per day.

Side Effects / Safety:
Gamma oryzanol appears to be a well-tolerated natural supplement, with no health-significant side effects.

Glutamine

syn. L-glutamine
syn. 2-amino-4-carbamoyl-butanoic acid

PERFORMANCE VALIDATION SCORES	
Combined	8
Clinical Support Rating	5
Empirical Evidence Rating	3

Description:

Glutamine is a common dietary amino acid. In humans, it is the most abundant amino acid in the extracellular pool. Furthermore, over 90% of the whole-body glutamine content is found in the muscles.[365] Glutamine is classified as a conditionally essential amino acid, which means that while the body is normally capable of manufacturing enough to meet its metabolic needs, under certain conditions (such as catabolic or immune-compromised states) it must be supplied in the diet.[366] This amino acid is active beyond its role as a component of tissue proteins, and is involved in a variety of metabolic functions including the support of immunity, gastrointestinal integrity, insulin secretion, neurological activity, and muscle protein synthesis.[367]

Glutamine has been shown to exert several biological activities that, at least in theory, might be of benefit to an exercising individual. To begin with, glutamine supports the synthesis of proteins in muscle cells.[368] It is also involved in the osmotic regulation of cell volume. Increasing glutamine pools may result in cell swelling.[369] This effect increases cell size and potentially also the rate of protein synthesis.[370] Some studies also suggest an ability for glutamine supplementation to manipulate tissue insulin sensitivity, which may help to partition nutrients away from fat storage and towards the muscles and liver.[371] Glutamine may also reduce muscle protein breakdown rates, an effect that may be mediated in part via the inhibition of myostatin, a protein that negatively influences muscle protein retention.[372]

Cellular metabolism and energy production are also influenced by glutamine in several other ways. For example, glutamine is an intermediary in the citric acid (TCA) cycle, and is utilized for energy by some cells.[373] Glutamine is also involved in glucose metabolism, and its supplementation has been shown to increase the storage of whole-body glycogen.[374] An increase in the cellular glutamine pool may also increase the exercise-induced release of IL-6 (Interleukin-6), a hormone-like cytokine involved in inflammation.[375] While low resting IL-6 levels are desirable for health, brief IL-6 elevations immediately following training may increase glucose disposal and fatty acid oxidation.[376] Glutamine may also help combat the buildup of ammonia, a waste product of anaerobic energy metabolism.[377] It can also increase antioxidant activity through conversion to glutathione.[378]

Glutamine is also very important to human digestion and immunity. Glutamine depletion after prolonged endurance exercise has been associated with suppression of the immune system. In some studies, the supplementation of glutamine has been shown to stimulate the immune system and reduce the incidence of illness following prolonged endurance exercise.[379, 380] Glutamine supplementation may also support the health and integrity of the intestinal lining.[381] It is often used in hospitals for its ability to support gastrointestinal health and nutritional absorption in patients with gastrointestinal disease, burn-trauma, or HIV/AIDS.[382] Because glutamine is so readily utilized by the intestines, liver, and kidneys, its bioavailability in serum is fairly low. It is estimated that as little as 10% of the administered dose may reach the muscles intact.[383]

Supplements containing glutamine are widely used in sports nutrition to enhance muscle growth, immunity, and recovery following intense exercise. Glutamine levels do decline with intense exercise,[384] and supplementation of this amino acid has been shown to increase muscle glutamine pools.[385] The potential anabolic and performance-enhancing benefits to this, however, remain the subject of much debate. An ergogenic effect has been demonstrated with glutamine supplementation, but such benefits have been very inconsistent. In spite of this inconsistency, glutamine appears to be a supplement with significant potential, especially for those undergoing intense weight training programs or high-level endurance activities.

Glutamine is available in both free amino acid form, and in the form of glutamine peptides (protein bound). Studies suggest that the bioavailability of free glutamine is considerably higher than that of glutamine peptides.[386] Most clinical studies have also been conducted with free L-glutamine, supporting the preferred use of this type of glutamine supplement. Benefits have also been noted in clinical studies with glutamine peptides, however, so both are likely to offer some effect. Further research is needed to better understand the therapeutic advantages and disadvantages to both types of glutamine, as well as the overall ergogenic value of this conditionally essential amino acid.

Promoted Benefits:
Glutamine is promoted to increase muscle mass and strength, and improve athletic performance.

Clinical Studies:
This ingredient has been shown to improve performance in placebo-controlled studies with trained adults. Its Clinical Support Rating is 5 (5/5).

One placebo-controlled study examined the effects of glutamine on exercise performance in a group of competitive soccer players.[387] The glutamine was added to a carbohydrate drink in the form of peptides, which was taken 30 minutes prior to exercise evaluations. This consisted of motorized treadmill running, along with measurements of oxygen consumption. The glutamine content of the drink was 3.5 grams, which was combined with 50 grams of maltodextrin. A drink containing only 50 grams of maltodextrin was used as a control group. The athletes taking the glutamine enhanced drink noticed a statistically significant improvement in total distance covered (15571 m versus 12750 m) and exercise duration before exhaustion (88 min versus 73 min).

Another study with positive findings examined the effects of glutamine supplementation on protein balance and glycogen storage following exercise in a group of healthy men.[388] The subjects exercised on a stationary cycle ergometer for 90 minutes at 65% peak oxygen consumption (VO2peak). After exercise, they consumed a carbohydrate (1 g/kg of body weight) and essential amino acid recovery drink (9.25 grams). In one group, glutamine was added to the drink at a dose of .3 g/kg of body weight. The study found that while the addition of glutamine failed to improve protein or glycogen synthesis rates, it did result in less muscle tissue breakdown (an anti-catabolic effect) during a three-hour monitored recovery period. In theory, this should result in a greater net protein gain from exercise.

Studies with glutamine have had conflicting results, with some investigations (often with short-term supplementation protocols) failing to find statistically significant improvements in exercise performance.[389, 390, 391, 392] Whether these inconsistent results are due to individual factors, study methodological difficulties, or specific circumstances in which glutamine can exert tangible ergogenic effects remains unclear. Further research is needed to better understand the potential role of glutamine in improving exercise performance.

Empirical Evidence:

Glutamine is widely available as a stand-alone nutritional supplement. The feedback on glutamine as an ergogenic aid has been mixed. In fact, glutamine may be defined as a "love it or hate it" type of supplement. Many bodybuilders find it to be a regular and important component of their exercise support and recovery drinks. Among this group, glutamine is said to help preserve muscle mass during periods of high activity, and sometimes even produce visible improvements in muscle size and strength during bulking phases of training. Glutamine also appears to be popular with many prolonged endurance and high intensity athletes, helping to both support optimal metabolism and reduce the incidence of infections and illness. For many athletes of all types, it is also commonly used to protect intestinal health, with the understanding that optimal absorption of nutrients is key to maximizing recovery, growth, and performance. It seems that an equally strong and vocal percentage of users, however, believe glutamine to be completely without noticeable effect and merit as an ergogenic supplement.

It is difficult to speculate as to why these opinions tend to vary so strongly. Given the low bioavailability of oral glutamine, insufficient dosage may be an issue, at least in some of these reports. Glutamine has an Empirical Evidence Rating of 3 (3/5).

Effective Dosage:

Based on clinical studies, a dosage of 10-30 g per day is recommended.

Side Effects / Safety:

Glutamine was well tolerated during clinical studies, with no significant side effects reported.[393]

Glycerol

syn. glycerin/glycerine
syn. 1,2,3-propanetriol

Description:

Glycerol is an organic compound of the alcohol family (it is specifically classified as a trihydric 3-carbon alcohol). It occurs naturally in the human body, and serves as a backbone component of triglycerides and cell phospholipids. Glycerol is abundant in nature, and can be found (in the form of glycerol esters) in all animal fats and vegetable oils. Glycerol is a sweet odorless clear viscous fluid, with a density of approximately 1.25 grams per milliliter. It is considered a caloric macronutrient, supplying approximately 4 calories per gram. It is commonly used as an ingredient in prepared foods, and also in the manufacture of cosmetic and drug products. It is also used as a sports nutrition product to improve endurance and slow dehydration.

Glycerol is classified as a hyperosmotic and osmotic diuretic agent. When administered in a sufficient dosage, glycerol induces an osmotic gradient. It can draw fluids into plasma, and may reduce the excretion of urine by enhancing the reabsorption of water in the nephrons.[394] As an osmotic, glycerol has some direct medical value in the treatment of many health ailments. This includes cerebral edema due to stroke, elevated intraocular pressure/glaucoma, intracranial hypertension, and postural hypotension (sudden drop in blood pressure when changing position, usually from sitting to standing). It is also applied to improve the hydration status of patients during certain types of acute gastrointestinal disease.

The ability of glycerol to act as an osmotic agent also lends it some tangible value as a sports ergogen. In this context, it is widely used by endurance athletes to increase the retention of water before an endurance event. This enhanced-hydration effect is referred to as "glycerol hyperhydration", and requires the co-consumption of a high volume of water. When properly applied, glycerol hyperhydration will result in a significant but temporary water increase and expansion of the plasma volume. It is important to note that the consumption of glycerol without water loading can actually have a mild diuretic effect, increasing urine outflow by decreasing the reabsorption of water by the kidneys. This could be counterproductive for fluid balance and endurance performance.

Clinical studies strongly support the effectiveness of common glycerol hyperhydration protocols for increasing water retention. This practice typically involves the loading of 1 g/kg of glycerol and approximately 1.5 L of water 1-2 hours prior to an endurance event.[395] This has been shown to result in a net increase of up to 900 mL of total body water compared to hydrating with water alone.[396] While the exercise and glycerol loading studies are not all in agreement about how this affects performance, there have been clear instances in which this additional fluid has slowed dehydration, reduced heat stress, and improved endurance. Taken as a whole, the studies do suggest that glycerol is effective for pre-event hydration, and may be especially useful at reducing dehydration and improving performance when access to water is limited during competition.

As a macronutrient, glycerol is classified as a carbohydrate. While this designation is sometimes contested based on the metabolic characteristics of this nutrient, it is appropriate given its structure. Glycerol can be utilized for energy via metabolism to glucose in the liver, although this is not an efficient path of metabolism. Because of this, it has only a minor effect on blood sugar levels compared to traditional carbohydrates.[397] It also does not serve as a significant energy source during intense exercise.[398] Given these properties, glycerol is widely regarded as a "low impact" carbohydrate, possessing reduced net caloric value. As such, it is not a suitable substitute for traditional carbohydrates with regard to glycogen replenishment or energy provision.

Glycerol syrup has a very sweet taste. Given that it is also regarded as a low impact carbohydrate source, it is widely used as a sweetener and sugar substitute in reduced calorie food products and meal replacement supplements. Since FDA regulations do stipulate that the glycerol content must be included in the total carbohydrate count on product labeling, many manufacturers include a second "net impact carbohydrates" listing on their products. This typically does not include low impact carbohydrates such as glycerol and sugar alcohols. The exact energy impact of glycerol is the subject of much debate, however, and likely varies depending on the metabolic conditions of the user. It

cannot be assumed to be completely devoid of caloric influence.

In addition to free glycerol, some manufacturers sell glycerol monostearate (GMS), which is glycerol attached to stearic acid. This is a powdered form of glycerol, better suited for tabletted, encapsulated, or powdered products. Glycerol monostearate contains approximately 25% glycerol by weight. It has not been studied for its potential performance-enhancing properties, or as a hyperhydrating agent prior to endurance competition. A large dose would be necessary to reach the equivalents of common glycerol hyperhydration protocols. It is reasonable to conclude, however, that the inclusion of GMS may still offer some osmotic/plasma-expanding effect in a sports nutrition formula depending on the dosage and additional ingredients used.

Promoted Benefits:
Glycerol is promoted to increase hydration prior to endurance exercise, slowing dehydration, reducing heat stress, and improving overall performance.

Clinical Studies:
Glycerol has been the subject of extensive clinical study. Glycerol hyperhydration has been shown to improve performance in placebo-controlled studies with trained adults. Its Clinical Support Rating is 5 (5/5).

One placebo-controlled study examined the effects of glycerol hyperhydration on exercise performance in a group of Olympic triathletes.[399] The subjects consumed glycerol (1.2 g/kg of bodyweight), along with 25 mL/kg of diluted carbohydrate-electrolyte drink (Gatorade .75 g/kg) during a 60-minute period two hours prior to competition. The subjects competed in two separate distance triathlons 2 weeks apart, each consisting of a 1.5-km swim, a 40-km bicycle ride, and a 10-km run. One triathlon was under warm temperature conditions (77 degrees Fahrenheit), and the other hot conditions (87 degrees). Given the increased temperature, subjects were under greater heat strain during the second triathlon, and noticed lower performance as a result. The subjects taking glycerol had significantly greater retention of water compared to those consuming the placebo. This was associated with better performance during the second triathlon, as noted by a significantly lower increase in total race time (+1:47 min glycerol vs. +11:40 min placebo). The greatest improvements of performance were noted during the final 10-km run, when involuntary dehydration should have reached their highest levels.

Another placebo-controlled crossover study examined the effects of glycerol hyperhydration during exercise in a hot environment.[400] Each subject pre-hydrated with water (24.1 ml/kg bodyweight) 2.5 hours prior to prolonged exercise at 60% Vo2max (equivalent in comfortable environment). When glycerol was added to the hydration regimen, there was an elevated sweat rate and reduced rectal temperature during exercise, suggesting that glycerol improved thermoregulation and reduced the impact of heat stress during exertion in a hot climate.

In another placebo-controlled study, the effect of glycerol hyperhydration on performance was examined in a group of competitive cyclists.[401] Subjects consumed 1 g/kg of glycerol along with 22 mL/kg of diluted Gatorade prior to exercise evaluations, which consisted of two 60-minute cycle ergometer time trials at constant and variable workloads. Glycerol hyperhydration resulted in a 600 mL increase in total body water over hydration with water alone. The glycerol group also noticed a 5% improvement in performance during the variable workload phase compared to placebo, though the researchers could not attribute this to a reduction in core temperature or lower cardiac output.

The clinical studies are in strong agreement that glycerol hyperhydration increases the retention of water over hydration with water alone. Many studies, however, conflict (in whole or in part) with studies such as the above, showing no improvements in temperature regulation or athletic performance. Why some studies show these improvements while others do not remains unclear. This may be due methodological difficulties, the rate or timing of hydration, or varying environmental or physiological circumstances in which glycerol hyperhydration can significantly improve performance. Some studies do suggest that the advantages are most apparent when access to water during competition is limited, and may be negligible when fluids are readily available and consumed during the activity.[402]

Overall, clinical studies do suggest that glycerol hyperhydration prior to prolonged endurance competition can delay dehydration and potentially even improve performance, especially when access to water may be limited during the activity. Further research is needed to better understand the optimal conditions for applying glycerol hyperhydration protocols.

Empirical Evidence:
Glycerol hyperhydration has been widely applied prior to prolonged endurance activities. The feedback on its use has been strongly positive. A majority of users report noticeable improvements with regard to involuntary dehydration, perceived sense of thirst, thermal stress, endurance, and overall athletic performance. A minority of users do not find glycerol hyperhydration useful, often because the practice induces strong gastrointestinal side effects that hinder comfort and performance. Since the majority of users experience minor or no side effects, as well as improved performance, glycerol hyperhydration has become an established practice in many areas of athletic competition (governing athletic rules permit-

ting). Glycerol has an Empirical Evidence Rating of 5 (5/5).

Effective Dosage:

Based on clinical studies, a dosage of 1 g/kg (body-weight) of glycerol along with 21-26 mL/kg (1-2 liters total) of water or a diluted carbohydrate-electrolyte drink (such as Gatorade with added water) over 2 hours prior to an endurance competition is recommended. An equivalent/effective dosage of glycerol monostearate has not been established.

Side Effects / Safety:

Glycerol is considered safe in doses below 5 g/kg of bodyweight.[403] Although glycerol hyperhydration is generally well tolerated, some individuals do report gastrointestinal distress (bloating, nausea, cramping, diarrhea), or other non-GI related side effects such as headache and blurred vision.[404,405,406]

Glycine-Arginine-Alpha-Ketoisocaproic Acid

syn. GAAKA
syn. Glycine-Arginine-Alpha-Ketoisocaproate

Description:

Glycine-arginine-alpha-ketoisocaproic acid (GAAKA) is an arginine and glycine salt of alpha-ketoisocaproic acid, a metabolite of L-leucine. The body will metabolize this compound into free arginine, alpha-ketoisocaproate, and glycine. Arginine is involved in a number of biological activities important to athletic performance, including protein synthesis, ammonia detoxification, nitric oxide production, growth hormone release, and the synthesis of creatine phosphate.[407] Ketoisocaproate has been speculated to improve anaerobic energy metabolism, and buffer exercise induced muscle damage.[408] Glycine is a non-essential amino acid involved in growth hormone synthesis, and may reduce muscle fatigue. GAAKA appears to reduce muscle fatigue and improve performance when taken prior to exercise.

Promoted Benefits:

Glycine-arginine-alpha-ketoisocaproic acid is promoted to reduce ammonia levels and improve muscle stamina during intense exercise.

Clinical Studies:

This ingredient has been shown to improve performance in placebo-controlled studies with untrained adults. It has a Clinical Support Rating of 4 (4/5).

One study involved the single-dose supplementation of GAAKA in a group of healthy subjects prior to exercise.[409] Muscle performance was measured with a series of three sets of knee concentric and eccentric contractions, which were conducted over a 15-minute period (five minutes of rest between sets). The supplementation of GAAKA was shown to increase the resistance to fatigue by 14-28% over the 3 sets, and total work by 9-12% (average 10.5%), compared to placebo.

A second study also examined the effects of a single-dose of GAAKA prior to exercise, which was taken by a group of healthy men.[410] The dosage administered was 11.2 g, which was consumed during a 45-minute period prior to exercise. The exercise protocol involved a series (five) of 10-second cycle ergometer sprints against high resistance. Evaluations were made of mean muscle power, peak power, serum lactate, and fatigue values. Subjects taking GAAKA noticed a greater retention of mean power between the first and second sprints. No other variables were significantly different from placebo.

These studies support the use of glycine-arginine-alpha-ketoisocaproic acid as a sport supplement.

Empirical Evidence:

Glycine-arginine-alpha-ketoisocaproic acid has been widely used as a stand-alone supplement. The feedback on this product has generally been mixed. Some users confirm that glycine-arginine-alpha-ketoisocaproic acid does improve muscle endurance and stamina when taken before intense training. A fair percentage of these further report that this increase in stamina allows for greater levels of stimulation during exercise, and thus enhanced results over time. The improvements are not immense, however, but consistent. A seemingly equal percentage of users report dissatisfaction with the supplement, often claiming a lack of substantial improvement. Whether this is due to individual insensitivity to GAAKA or unrealistic expectations remains unclear. Glycine-arginine-alpha- ketoisocaproic acid has an Empirical Evidence Rating of 3 (3/5).

Effective Dosage:
Based on clinical studies, a dosage of 11.2 grams is recommended once daily, prior to intense exercise.

Side Effects / Safety:
Glycine-arginine-alpha-ketoisocaproic acid was well tolerated during clinical studies, with no significant side effects reported.

Glycine Propionyl-L-Carnitine

syn. GPLC

syn. Glycine-PLC

PERFORMANCE VALIDATION SCORES	
Combined	9
Clinical Support Rating	5
Empirical Evidence Rating	4

Description:

Glycine propionyl-L-carnitine (GPLC) consists of propionyl-L-carnitine (PLC) bonded with the amino acid glycine. The body ultimately breaks these bonds, so that the active constituents are provided to cells in their free (utilizable) forms. PLC and glycine both may have vasodilatory properties, which can increase blood flow to peripheral tissues.[411,412] This may aid endurance performance by helping to supply oxygen to the muscles, and also assist in the delivery of nutrients to muscles that are damaged/repairing. Studies suggest that the supplementation of GPLC can induce vasodilation by increasing nitric oxide levels. They also support some acute performance enhancing benefits in healthy trained adults, although further evidence is needed to confirm significant ergogenic value with regular use.

Propionyl-L-carnitine is the propionate ester of carnitine, a cofactor in the metabolism and transport of fatty acids. Among other things, carnitine helps with the transport of certain long-chain fatty acids. It also enhances fatty acid oxidation, which may allow more ATP to be available for muscle cells. The propionic acid form of carnitine appears to have a higher affinity for muscle carnitine transferase, and thus may be more effective at increasing local tissue concentrations.[413] Propionic acid is also a substrate for the formation of succinate, which is involved in the Krebs energy cycle. As such, its addition may help provide energy during hypoxic (low oxygen) conditions. PLC has been shown to increase exercise capacity in certain diseased states, such as peripheral arterial disease.[414]

Glycine is the smallest of the 20 common amino acids used in the manufacture of proteins. It is a non-essential amino acid, and is readily synthesized from serine when dietary intake is insufficient. Glycine is also an important neurotransmitter in the central nervous system, and is involved with the biosynthesis of many compounds including certain peptides, creatine, bile salts, glycogen, hemoglobin, ATP, and nucleic acids. Research suggests that glycine supplementation might possess some ergogenic value with regard to protein utilization, energy, metabolism, and endurance. Studies with exercising adults, however, have had conflicting and unclear results.[415]

Promoted Benefits:

Glycine propionyl-L-carnitine is promoted to increase nitric oxide synthesis, peripheral blood flow, and cellular energy, as well as to improve fatty acid and carbohydrate metabolism, reduce muscle tissue damage (anti-catabolic), increase the removal of lactate, and improve overall sports/exercise performance.

Clinical Studies:

This ingredient has been shown to improve performance in placebo-controlled studies with trained adults. Its Clinical Support Rating is 5 (5/5).

The most widely referenced placebo-controlled performance study published on glycine propionyl-L-carnitine involved its supplementation by a group of experienced resistance-trained men.[416] Each subject consumed a single dose of 4.5 g before being evaluated for exercise performance, which involved a series of five 10-second cycle ergometer sprints against resistance. Subjects taking GPLC noticed a 2.6-15% increase in peak and mean anaerobic power compared to placebo. There were also statistically significant and strong trends of reduced serum lactate (15.7-16.2%) with GPLC supplementation.

A second placebo-controlled study failed to find significant benefit to glycine propionyl-L-carnitine supplementation.[417] It examined the effects of two dosage levels of GPLC (1 g and 3 g) on exercise performance in a group of healthy men and women. The subjects consumed the supplement for a period of eight weeks, during which time they also were subject to an aerobic exercise program. After eight weeks they were evaluated for muscle carnitine levels (vastus lateralis), VO2peak (peak oxygen consumption), exercise time to fatigue, anaerobic threshold, anaerobic power, and total work. Neither dose improved muscle carnitine levels or any marker of aerobic or anaerobic exercise performance compared to placebo.

With regard to vasodilation, we find another relevant placebo-controlled study that examined the effects of continued glycine propionyl-L-carnitine intake by a group of healthy resistance-trained men.[418] This investigation was focused on measuring serum nitrate (NOx) levels at rest and after exercise, which is a marker for nitric oxide production. The subjects consumed 4.5 g of GPLC per day for a period of four weeks. The exercise stimulus involved the use of an isometric handgrip dynamometer. The supplementation of glycine propionyl-L-carnitine tended to produce higher levels of NOx (and thus nitric oxide) after exercise compared to subjects taking placebo.

Although not all reports are in agreement, clinical studies do support the use of glycine propionyl-L-carnitine to improve acute exercise performance. Further research is needed to confirm if the regular use of GPLC can provide ergogenic value to trained adults.

Empirical Evidence:

Glycine propionyl-L-carnitine is widely available as a stand-alone nutritional supplement. The feedback on its use as a sport supplement tends to be positive. The main points of positive feedback usually involve its properties as a vasodilator (to increase the workout muscle "pump" effect), and ability to improve performance during prolonged (endurance-type) exercise. The feedback of GPLC with regard to muscle growth and resistance-training results tends to be less consistently positive. A fair percentage of users fail to notice any benefit from GPLC use, even with regard to vasodilation. This appears to be consistent with a small percentage of "non-responders" noted in the nitrate studies discussed above. Whether this is due to an individual insensitivity to GPLC or other confounding variables remains unclear. Glycine propionyl-L-carnitine has an Empirical Evidence Rating of 4 (4/5).

Effective Dosage:

Based on clinical studies, a dosage of 4.5 g per day is recommended.

Side Effects / Safety:

Glycine propionyl-L-carnitine was well tolerated during clinical studies, with no significant side effects. Note that in higher doses, glycine sometimes causes gastrointestinal distress (nausea, vomiting, diarrhea) and a mild sedative effect.

HMB (beta-hydroxy-beta-methylbutyrate)

syn. β-Hydroxyisovaleric acid

PERFORMANCE VALIDATION SCORES	
Combined	**8**
Clinical Support Rating	5
Empirical Evidence Rating	3

Description:

HMB (beta-hydroxy-beta-methylbutyrate) is a naturally occurring metabolite of the essential branched-chain amino acid leucine. This nutrient is obtained in small amounts from a variety of food sources, including catfish, breast milk, and citrus fruits. The human body also produces HMB from leucine, which accounts for approximately 5% of its total metabolism. The approximate daily production of HMB in humans is estimated to range from 1/4 to 1 gram, depending on the concentration of protein (specifically leucine) in the diet.[419] As a byproduct of the metabolism of an essential nutrient, HMB is not considered an essential dietary nutrient itself. In supplemental form, HMB is most often supplied as a calcium salt.

The exact role of HMB in exercise physiology is not fully understood. It appears to influence a number of biological processes, particularly those involved in muscle repair and resistance to damage. However, its exact mechanism of action in these processes is unknown. HMB appears to exert some of its activity via stimulation of the MAPK and PI3K pathways, and increasing the expression of IGF-1 mRNA levels.[420,421]

This leads to reduced muscle cell damage and increased myoblast (a precursor cell used for repair/growth) production. It has been shown to support a positive protein balance, specifically by reducing the protein catabolism phase of protein turnover.[422] HMB has also been demonstrated to reduce creatine phosphokinase (a marker of muscle damage) and inhibit lactate dehydrogenase (an enzyme responsible for forming lactate in the muscles) after intense endurance exercise.[423]

HMB has long been the subject of controversy, mainly concerning the manner in which it was marketed early on. Much of this has been attributed to former EAS owner Bill Phillips, who compared HMB to Deca-Durabolin, a popular anabolic steroid, when first introducing the readers of his magazine (*Muscle-Media 2000*) to the new supplement. The supplement, of course, failed to perform in any manner that resembled this drug, which resulted in a great deal of negative backlash towards Phillips and HMB. For years, this public relations disaster overshadowed much of the active research on this substance, some of it very positive. Today, the phrase "feels like Deca" has become synonymous with the exaggeration of a supplement's efficacy.

Promoted Benefits:

HMB is promoted to help increase muscle mass, strength, endurance, and aerobic performance.

Clinical Studies:

HMB has been the subject of extensive clinical study. A number of placebo-controlled investigations support the use of this supplement to enhance exercise/athletic performance. This ingredient has been shown to improve performance in placebo-controlled studies with experienced resistance-trained adults. Its Clinical Support Rating is 5 (5/5).

One placebo-controlled investigation published in May 2009 examined the effect of nine weeks of HMB supplementation in resistance-trained men.[424] The consumption of 3 grams of HMB per day tended to produce a small increase in average strength (1.6%) compared to placebo. The increase was mainly attributed to improvements in lower body strength, which improved on an average of 9.1%. Measures of upper body strength (bench press, bicep curl) were inconclusive. Fat free mass increased only slightly (.2%) over placebo.

The *Journal of Strength Conditioning Research* conducted a comprehensive analysis of all HMB studies involving resistance training published prior to May 2009.[425] Nine qualifying placebo-controlled studies were reviewed, involving a total of 394 participants. A combined evaluation of all studies showed a slight average increase in strength (3.7%) with HMB supplementation. The most consistent improvements were noticed in the lower body strength measures of untrained subjects. When applied to individuals with training experience, positive outcomes in strength measures were less consistent, and usually minor. Researchers could not detect any significant effect of HMB on muscle mass or body composition.

With regard to its effects on aerobic metabolism, a placebo-controlled study examined the effects of five weeks of HMB supplementation (3g/day) on running performance in a group of active college students.[426] Each subject completed interval training on a tread-mill, and oxygen consumption was measured with the use of a respiratory-gas analyzer. Supplementation with HMB resulted in an 8.4% increase in maximal oxygen consumption (Vo2max).

Empirical Evidence:

HMB has been widely used as a stand-alone product. The empirical evidence on this supplement has been mixed. Many users do report positive results, particularly with muscle endurance and overall athletic/exercise performance. The improvements are typically modest and difficult to accurately quantify, but tangible to these users nonetheless. Many become loyal repeat users of HMB. A seemingly equal percentage of users, however, do not seem to notice strong positive results with this supplement. Given that only modest improvements appeared during clinical studies with trained subjects, it is possible that benefits are imparted to a greater percentage of users, but they are overlooked. HMB has an Empirical Evidence Rating of 3 (3/5).

Effective Dosage:

Based on clinical studies, a dosage of 3 grams per day is recommended.

Side Effects / Safety:

HMB was well tolerated in all clinical studies, with no significant adverse effects.

Icariin

syn. Horny Goat Weed (extract)
syn. Epimedium extract

PERFORMANCE VALIDATION SCORES	
Combined	5
Clinical Support Rating	2
Empirical Evidence Rating	3

Description:

Icariin is a natural flavonoid compound found in several herbaceous plants of the epimedium species (commonly known as Horny Goat Weed). Epimedium extracts have a long history of use in traditional Chinese medicine, where they have been widely applied to treat erectile dysfunction and increase male libido. They have also been used to treat numerous other medical conditions including cough, asthma, high blood pressure, and heart disease. In sports nutrition, epimedium extracts (standardized for icariin) are promoted to increase male testosterone levels and improve exercise performance. Common sources of icariin specifically include extracts of epimedium sagittatum, epimedium grandiflorum, and epimedium brevicornum.

Modern studies suggest icariin has a broad range of biological activity. For example, animal studies have shown icariin to support erection via a nitric oxide simulating and phosphodiesterase (PDE5) inhibiting effect, similar to the prescription drugs sildendafil and tadalafil.[427,428] Other animal studies have shown icariin to counter some of the negative metabolic effects of stress, specifically reducing levels of cortisol and the inflammatory mediators interleukin-6 (IL-6) and tumor-necrosis-factor alpha (TNF-alpha).[429] This could have a number of positive health implications. Additionally, icariin seems to possess antioxidant[430] and bone-strengthening properties.[431] It may also possess some estrogenic activity.[432,433] Studies on the effects of epimedium extracts on serum androgen levels have been conflicting, however, and it is unknown if icariin possesses tangible ergogenic value.

Promoted Benefits:

Icariin is promoted to increase testosterone levels and support the anabolic effects of resistance exercise.

Clinical Studies:

The use of icariin as a sport supplement is supported by animal data only. Its Clinical Support Rating is 2 (2/5).

One of the most widely cited studies on icariin examined its effects on sexual function and serum androgen levels in male rats. The experiment involved drug-induced damage to the reproductive system, followed by supplementation with either icariin (200 mg/kg daily) or testosterone (5 mg per day). Icariin was shown to increase serum testosterone levels, and improved other variables including bone resorption and reproductive organ condition in a similar manner as subcutaneous testosterone injection.

Other clinical studies have had conflicting results, however, showing epimedium extracts and icariin to have no effect on serum testosterone levels.[434,435] No peer reviewed placebo-controlled human studies examining the effects of this supplement on androgen levels or exercise performance have been published. Further research is needed to determine if icariin has testosterone stimulating or ergogenic effects in humans.

Empirical Evidence:

Icariin (in the form of standardized epimedium extracts) is widely available as a stand-alone nutritional supplement. The feedback on its use as a sport supplement has been very mixed. A majority of users do seem to report erectile stimulating properties, and icariin supplements (usually marketed as Horny Goat Weed) are commonly used in male aphrodisiac and erectile dysfunction treating supplements. This, however, has not translated into common anecdotal reports of high testosterone elevations or noticeable muscle gain / improved exercise performance. While some users do report such activity, the frequency is too low to consider this a positive trend. Icariin has an Empirical Evidence Rating of 3 (3/5).

Effective Dosage:

An effective dosage of this supplement has not been established. Manufacturers commonly recommend 50-200 mg of icariin per day. Note that there are many different extracts of varying purities, which makes evaluating and dosing this supplement somewhat difficult.

Side Effects / Safety:

Icariin appeared to be well tolerated during clinical studies, with no significant toxicity or side effects reported.[436]

Ipriflavone

syn. 7-isopropoxyisoflavone

Description:

Ipriflavone (7-isopropoxyisoflavone) is an isoflavonoid from soy. Isoflavonoids belong to a much larger family of flavonoids, which are a group of natural polyphenolic compounds widely found in fruits and vegetables. These compounds generally have antioxidant activities, and may be responsible for some of the health-promoting aspects of fruits and vegetables. Depending on individual structure, many flavonoid compounds also possess additional biological activity. Flavonoids are extremely common and diverse in structure, however, which makes determining the potential unique biological activity of each very difficult.

Ipriflavone is considered a phytoestrogen (a plant estrogen). In humans it does not appear to be appreciably estrogenic, but does support some estrogen-linked biological functions. Its most notable activity is the support of calcium retention in bones. Although its exact mode of action in this process is unknown, it appears in part to increase the absorption of calcium from the intestinal tract.[437] It also appears to directly support bone mineral density, both by activating mature osteoclast cells, and by stimulating the formation of new osteoclasts via estrogen-induced calcitonin secretion.[438] Ipriflavone is regarded as a medicinal product in several countries including Italy, Japan, and Hungary, where it is commonly used to treat osteoporosis.[439]

Ipriflavone has been widely promoted by sports nutrition manufacturers to improve exercise performance, especially with regard to increasing muscle mass and strength. There is, however, little clinical or empirical evidence to link such muscle-anabolic activity to this compound. While it has been shown to increase IGF-1 expression (Insulin-Like Growth Factor-1, an anabolic hormone) in bone during animal studies, no muscle-supportive metabolic changes have been documented in peer-reviewed studies with the use of this phytoestrogen in humans. Presently, it is unknown if there is any anabolic or performance-enhancing activity inherent in ipriflavone.

Promoted Benefits:

Ipriflavone is promoted to help increase muscle mass, strength, and athletic performance.

Clinical Studies:

The use of ipriflavone as a sport supplement is supported by animal data only. Its Clinical Support Rating is 2 (2/5).

Sport supplement manufacturers commonly cite the original 1970's patents for this supplement when discussing its anabolic activity.[440,441] This data cannot be considered reliable, however, as it does not come from a peer-reviewed scientific study, and may be the subject of bias. It is also well understood that the United States Patent Office is focused much more on the novelty and unobvious nature of an invention that validating the scientific methods contained in it.

One peer reviewed clinical study that could be supportive of ipriflavone is a paper disclosing its effect on bone IGF-1 expression in rats.[442] As part of this investigation, some animals were given injections of this isoflavonoid at a dose of 100 mg/kg of body weight daily for 65 days. Animals given ipriflavone were shown to have more IGF-1 in the femur bone than those not receiving the injections. In this study, the IGF-1 increase was not accompanied by an increase in bone mineral density.

This information is far from conclusive. More research is needed to determine if there is any ergogenic value to the use of ipriflavone in exercising humans.

Empirical Evidence:
Ipriflavone has been widely used as a stand-alone product. Unfortunately, the feedback on the use of this compound as a sport supplement tends to be negative. Most users fail to notice any of the touted benefits with regard to muscle mass and strength gains, nor improvements in athletic performance. While a small percentage of users do seem to report that they may have received positive results, the frequency and consistency of such reports is low. As such, these positive reports could be the result of placebo effect. Ipriflavone has an Empirical Evidence Rating of 2 (2/5).

Effective Dosage:
An effective dosage of this supplement has not been established. Manufacturers commonly recommend 500-1,000 mg per day.

Side Effects / Safety:
Ipriflavone was well tolerated during clinical studies, with no significant side effects.[443] A small percentage of users appear to notice gastrointestinal distress (loose stool, nausea, diarrhea).

Leucine

syn. L-leucine
syn. 2-Amino-4-methylpentanoic acid

PERFORMANCE VALIDATION SCORES	
Combined	9
Clinical Support Rating	5
Empirical Evidence Rating	4

Description:

Leucine is an amino acid, one of eight that are considered essential components of the diet. Leucine is also one of three branched-chain amino acids (BCAA). These amino acids are highly prominent in skeletal muscle tissue, with leucine accounting for about 8% of the total muscle protein content.[444] BCAAs are structurally and functionally distinct from other amino acids, and are involved in a variety of biological processes, including skeletal muscle energy and protein metabolism. Leucine stands out from other branched-chain amino acids as the most active at stimulating protein synthesis within muscle cells.[445] Given this role, leucine supplements are widely used in sports nutrition to enhance muscle growth and recovery following intense exercise.

Exactly how muscle cells sense and respond to leucine is not fully understood. We do know that this amino acid stimulates the mammalian target of rapamycin (mTOR) signaling pathway, which is necessary for the initiation of muscle protein synthesis.[446] Leucine also seems to work synergistically with insulin to help stimulate protein synthesis and nutrient uptake within muscle cells after intense exercise.[447] It specifically seems to intensify the signal intensity of phosphatidylinositol-3 kinase (PI3K), which is triggered by insulin.[448] Leucine may also be metabolized for fuel when needed. Oxidation of this amino acid is increased significantly during exercise, in some direct correlation with whole-body oxygen consumption and energy demands.[449]

While studies may be conflicting, leucine appears to be a strong supporter of muscle energy and anabolic processes. Under some circumstances, its supplementation may impart measurable muscle-building or performance-enhancing effects. It is of note, however, that some of the cellular anabolic pathways responsible for muscle growth appear to be better stimulated by all three branched-chain amino acids (leucine, isoleucine, and valine) compared to leucine alone.[450] Complete BCAA supplementation has also been more extensively studied, and its use is fairly well supported in the medical literature. While leucine may indeed have beneficial effects in exercising humans, most bodybuilders and athletes prefer complete BCAA supplementation to pure leucine products.

Promoted Benefits:

Leucine is promoted to increase muscle mass and strength, and improve athletic performance.

Clinical Studies:

This ingredient has been shown to improve performance in placebo-controlled studies with trained adults. Its Clinical Support Rating is 5 (5/5).

One placebo-controlled study examined the effects of leucine supplementation in a group of competitive outrigger canoeists.[451] Subjects took a dosage of 45 mg/kg of bodyweight per day, which equates to slightly less than 4 grams for a person of about 185 lbs in weight. This level of supplementation was continued for a period of six weeks. Exercise evaluations included upper body power testing with a row to exhaustion at 70-75% maximal oxygen consumption. In this study, subjects taking leucine noticed statistically significant improvements in upper body power and exercise endurance compared to those taking placebo. Rowing time to exhaustion was increased from 77.6 min to 88.3 minutes, and perceived exertion decreased.

With regard to protein kinetics, another placebo-controlled study examined the effects of the branched-chain amino acid leucine on protein synthesis and retention following resistance training.[452] The leucine was added to a whey protein/carbohydrate recovery drink. The study also examined the same protein/carbohydrate drink without leucine, as well as a carbohydrate only drink. The exercise protocols consisted of eight sets each of leg press and leg extensions, which were performed at approximately 80% 1-rep maximum weight for approximately eight reps each. Subjects consumed the supplemental drink every 30 minutes after training, for a total of 6 hours. Measures of protein kinetics were taken at various points over this six-hour window. The leucine-enriched drink resulted in the greatest overall retention of muscle protein.

Studies with leucine have had conflicting results, with some failing to find statistically significant improvements in exercise performance following supplementation.[453,454,455] Whether these inconsistent results are due to individual factors, study methodological difficulties, or specific circumstances in which leucine can exert tangible ergogenic effects remains unclear. Further research is needed to better understand the potential role of leucine in improving exercise performance.

Empirical Evidence:

Leucine is widely available as a stand-alone nutritional supplement. The feedback on leucine as an ergogenic aid tends to be positive. Leucine supplements are most commonly used with bodybuilders and power athletes looking to support muscle anabolism. In many cases, the user can attribute a visibly greater level of muscle gain when adding leucine to their regular post-exercise or during-training support drinks. It is of note, however, that many find the supplementation of all three branched-chain amino acids to be superior to leucine use alone. While both seem to provide tangible benefits for a majority of users, the results from complete BCAA supplementation tend to be better. A minority of users fail to notice any benefits with leucine supplementation (or BCAA supplementation for that matter). It may be that in some circumstances branched-chain amino acid manipulation alone will not provide enough added stimuli for sufficient muscle or performance improvements beyond that provided by optimal training and diet. Overall, leucine has an Empirical Evidence Rating of 4 (4/5).

Effective Dosage:

Based on clinical studies, a dosage of 3-10 g per day is recommended.

Side Effects / Safety:

Leucine was well tolerated during clinical studies, with no significant side effects reported. Higher doses may cause gastrointestinal distress.

Longjack

syn. Eurycoma Longifolia Jack
syn. Tongkat Ali

PERFORMANCE VALIDATION SCORES	
Combined	8
Clinical Support Rating	4
Empirical Evidence Rating	4

Description:

Longjack is a common name for the root extract of Eurycoma Longifolia Jack, a flowering plant native to Southeast Asia. Longjack is an old folk medicine in this part of the world. In Malaysia it is known as Tongkat Ali, which literally translates to "Ali's walking stick." It is commonly incorporated into a tea or paste, and used to treat a variety of ailments including malaria, ulcer, headache, fever, and dysentery. The Indonesians call it Pasak Bumi (which means firmly nailed to the ground), and use it to treat dysentery and malaria. Almost universally in Southeast Asia, it is also used as an aphrodisiac, to increase male sexual potency, and to treat impotence. Although this traditional medicine is centuries old, it remains in wide use in this region today.

Modern scientific evidence does seem to support the use of this traditional medicine. For example, studies show that the administration of this extract increases male sexual performance in animals.[456,457] Furthermore, they show increases in the primary male androgen (testosterone), and suggest that male sexual potency is enhanced by this action. Many other potential benefits of Eurycoma Longifolia have also been supported in the medical literature, including anti-tumor and anti-malarial activity.[458] And most relevant to its use as a sport supplement, studies suggest that longjack can help increase testosterone levels, lower cortisol, and improve the muscle mass and strength gains from exercise.

The main bioactive components in longjack are believed to be quassinoids, which are bitter principles found exclusively in plants of the Simaroubaceae family.[459] More than a dozen quassinoids have been identified in Eurycma Longifolia. The most discussed of these include eurycomalactone, euryconolactone (A-C), eurycomanon, and eurycomanol. Many of the plant's active components are also found in the form of bonded amino acid chains called glycopeptides. No relevant studies specific to quassinoid or glycopeptide fractions have been conducted, which makes standardizing longjack extracts for active component (s) difficult. Most manufacturers focus on the content of glycopeptides. Consumers are likely to notice varying levels of potency between products given different plant origins and extraction methods.

Promoted Benefits:

Longjack is promoted to elevate testosterone, lower cortisol, and increase muscle mass and strength.

Clinical Studies:

This ingredient has been shown to improve body composition and performance in a placebo-controlled study of untrained individuals. It has a Clinical Support Rating of 4 (4/5).

The above mentioned study involved giving a group of healthy men 100 mg of Eurycoma Longifolia water-soluble extract per day for five weeks.[460] They were subject to a controlled strength-training program (resistance exercise) on alternating days. Subjects taking longjack noticed statistically significant improvements in lean body mass (+2.13 kg) and bicep circumference (+1.8 cm), which were not noticed in the placebo group. The supplement group also noticed better overall strength gains (+6.78% vs. +2.77%) and fat loss (-1.36 BF %) in comparison.

Another placebo-controlled study involved the administration of a single 100 mg dose of a longjack extract to a group of male endurance athletes 30 minutes before exercise.[461] Subjects were made to cycle 14 miles in total, and levels of testosterone (a muscle building hormone) and cortisol (which breaks down muscle) were measured before and after every four laps, to assess any potential change to the anabolic/catabolic state. Longjack supplementation produced a statistically significant increase in testosterone levels (+16%), and a reduction in cortisol (-32.3%), compared to placebo. This study suggests that longjack can create a metabolic environment that is more favorable for the growth/retention of muscle mass.

Empirical Evidence:
Longjack is widely available as a stand-alone supplement. The feedback on this supplement tends to be positive. A majority of users taking a sufficient dosage of a quality Eurycoma Longifolia extract seem to attribute greater improvements in muscle mass and strength to their use of this supplement. It also often seems to show other signs of androgenic action, such as increased libido and mental energy. Although perhaps less common, many other users are unable to positively associate gains with their use of longjack supplements. Whether this is the result of low quality extracts or individual insensitivity (non-responsiveness) to Eurycoma Longifolia remains unclear. Longjack has an Empirical Evidence Rating of 4 (4/5).

Effective Dosage:
Based on clinical studies and empirical evidence, a dosage of 100-200 mg per day is recommended.

Side Effects / Safety:
Longjack was well tolerated during clinical studies, with no significant side effects reported.

Methoxyisoflavone

syn. 5-methyl-7-methoxyisoflavone

PERFORMANCE VALIDATION SCORES	
Combined	2
Clinical Support Rating	0
Empirical Evidence Rating	2

Description:

Methoxyisoflavone (5-methyl-7-methoxyisoflavone) is a flavonoid from soy. Flavonoids are a broad class of natural polyphenolic compounds widely found in fruits and vegetables. These compounds generally have antioxidant activities, and may be responsible for some of the health-promoting aspects of fruits and vegetables. Depending on individual structure, many flavonoid compounds also possess additional biological activity. Flavonoids are extremely common and diverse in structure, however, which makes determining the potential unique biological activity of each very difficult.

Methoxyisoflavone belongs to a specific flavonoid category called isoflavonoids. These compounds all share a common 3-phenylchromen-4-one backbone, and are found exclusively in the legume (bean) family. There have, unfortunately, been few specific studies on this particular isoflavonoid. Methoxyisoflavone has been widely promoted by sports nutrition manufacturers to improve exercise performance in humans, especially for increasing muscle mass and strength.

Presently, however, it is unclear if any anabolic or performance-enhancing activity is actually present in this substance.

Promoted Benefits:

Methoxyisoflavone is promoted to help increase muscle mass, strength, and athletic performance.

Clinical Studies:

The use of methoxyisoflavone as a sport supplement is not supported by peer-reviewed clinical studies. Its Clinical Support Rating is 0 (0/5).

Sport supplement manufacturers commonly cite two pieces of research to support the sale of methoxyisoflavone. The first is the original 1970's patents for this supplement.[462,463] This data cannot be considered reliable, however, as it does not come from a peer-reviewed scientific study, and may be the subject of bias. It is also well understood that the U.S. Patent Office is focused much more on the novelty and unobvious nature of an invention that validating the scientific methods contained in it.

The second is a placebo-controlled study published in 2001 that demonstrated a 1.3 kg lean body mass gain in resistance-trained men who took 800 mg/day of methoxyisoflavone for eight weeks.[464] This paper cannot be accepted as clinical validation, however, as it was only published as an abstract (there is no review of the methods), did not disclose the probability value for lean body mass gain (no way to determine what the authors considered statistically significant), and was authored in part by a representative of the supplement's manufacturer.

This leaves only one peer-reviewed published placebo-controlled study that examines the effects of methoxyisoflavone supplementation on exercising adults.[465] The study also involved supplementation for eight weeks (800 mg/day) in a group of men with resistance-training experience. A detailed resistance-training program was followed as part of the study, and measurements of strength and anaerobic performance were taken at various points. Investigators could not find any statistically significant or strong trends of improvement caused by methoxyisoflavone in any marker of performance, anabolic/catabolic status, or body composition. This study does not support the use of methoxyisoflavone as a sport supplement.

Empirical Evidence:
Methoxyisoflavone has been widely used as a stand-alone product. The empirical evidence on this supplement has been weak. Most users fail to notice any significant body composition or performance benefits from its use. A smaller percentage of users, however, do claim to see results from taking it. When reported, positive results are usually centered on muscle and strength gains, not necessarily anaerobic or aerobic performance. Methoxyisoflavone products remain in active commerce today. Whether this is the result of marketing hype, or tangible improvements and repeat consumer business, remains unclear. Methoxyisoflavone has an Empirical Evidence Rating of 2 (2/5).

Effective Dosage:
An effective dosage of this supplement has not been established. Manufacturers commonly recommend 800-1,000 mg per day.

Side Effects / Safety:
Methoxyisoflavone was well tolerated during clinical studies, with no reported side effects.

N-Acetylcysteine (NAC)

syn. N-acetyl-L-cysteine
syn. mercapturic acid

PERFORMANCE VALIDATION SCORES	
Combined	7
Clinical Support Rating	3
Empirical Evidence Rating	4

Description:

N-acetylcysteine (NAC) is the n-acetyl derivative of the amino acid L-cysteine. It serves as a precursor in the synthesis of glutathione, one of the body's primary antioxidant (free radical scavenging) molecules. N-acetylcysteine itself is considered to be a potent antioxidant, and may directly and indirectly help protect body tissues from oxidative damage. NAC is also regarded as an immunostimulatory compound,[466] and might help increase resistance to viral or bacterial infection. The potential health benefits of NAC supplementation are the subject of much ongoing research. In sports nutrition, n-acetylcysteine is commonly used to reduce oxidative stress subsequent to heavy training, and to increase exercise endurance.

N-acetylcysteine is sold as a drug product in many countries, and prescribed for a number of ailments. For example, it is commonly used to reduce the thickness of mucous in patients with pneumonia, flu, bronchitis, or other forms of respiratory congestion. It acts by breaking some of the protein disulfide bonds holding the mucous together. NAC is also widely used to protect and detoxify the liver, and even to treat cases of acetaminophen overdose or toxicity. It is also used to prevent kidney toxicity during contrast imaging in patients with impaired renal function. In addition to its accepted clinical uses, n-acetylcysteine is also being investigated for a host of other health conditions including cognitive dysfunction, diabetes, HIV infection, and cystic fibrosis.

While n-acetylcysteine has been the subject of compelling clinical studies with regard to ergogenic properties, specifically demonstrating an ability to reduce muscle fatigue in exercising adults, these investigations have tended to involve continuous intravenous (IV) infusions of NAC during exercise, which are impractical for general use. Additional research does suggest that the oral use of n-acetylcysteine supplements can also impart performance-enhancing benefits in exercising individuals. However, further research is needed to validate (and better understand) these potential properties of oral n-acetylcysteine.

Promoted Benefits:

N-acetylcysteine is promoted to reduce fatigue and increase muscle endurance during prolonged exercise.

Clinical Studies:

This ingredient has been shown in human placebo-controlled studies to improve metabolic markers (respiratory muscle fatigue, erythropoietin, hemoglobin) linked to positive changes in body composition or performance. It's Clinical Support Rating is 3 (3/5).

One placebo-controlled study examined the effects of oral n-acetylcysteine on various blood parameters in a group of healthy adults.[467] A dosage of 1,200 mg was used, which was taken for a period of eight days. The supplementation of NAC was shown to increase erythropoietin levels by 26%. This hormone stimulates the production of red blood cells. This result was accompanied by a 9% increase in both hemoglobin and hematocrit, representing a tangible increase in oxygen carrying capacity. This effect should enhance aerobic exercise performance.

Another placebo-controlled investigation looked at the effects of oral NAC on respiratory muscle fatigue during heavy exercise.[468] Subjects consumed 1,800 mg of n-acetylcysteine and exercised for 30 minutes at 85% maximum oxygen consumption (VO2max). Measurements of respiratory pressure were taken at rest and every five minutes during exercise. The supplementation of n-acetylcysteine maintained 14% higher inhalation pressure at 25 and 30 minutes of exercise, suggesting reduced respiratory fatigue. Studies have shown that respiratory muscle fatigue and reduced inhalation pressure can impair oxygen uptake and exercise performance.[469]

In addition to these oral supplementation studies, there have been a number of positive investigations with the intravenous infusion of n-acetylcysteine with exercise.[470, 471, 472] One of the most widely referenced studies examined the effects on NAC on exercise performance in a group of well-trained adults.[473] Subjects were given a 15-minute IV infusion of n-acetylcysteine beginning 20 minutes prior to exercise. The rate of delivery was 125 mg/kg per hour. After 15 minutes this was switched to a rate of 25 mg/kg per hour, which continued throughout exercise. The subjects were evaluated with the use of a stationary cycle ergometer, and initially performed at 71% peak oxygen consumption (VO2peak) for 45 minutes. This was followed by a cycle sprint at 92%

VO2peak until exhaustion. The subjects that were given n-acetylcysteine improved their time to exhaustion by an average of 23.8% compared to those given placebo.

While these results suggest ergogenic action with oral n-acetylcysteine, further research is needed to confirm such activity, and to understand the most ideal applications for using this supplement.

Empirical Evidence:
N-acetylcysteine is widely available as a stand-alone nutritional supplement. The feedback on its use as a sport supplement tends to be positive. Most athletic users seem to notice a reduction in muscle fatigue during exercise, especially those subject to prolonged endurance-type activities. NAC is also widely used by athletes and bodybuilders as a general health-supporting supplement, given its strong ability to act as an antioxidant and liver detox agent. While the feedback on this supplement is generally positive, many other users feel NAC offers no tangible ergogenic value. Whether this is due to an individual insensitivity to the supplement, or particular applications in which it is, and is not, metabolically useful, remains unclear. N-acetylcysteine has an Empirical Evidence Rating of 4 (4/5).

Effective Dosage:
Based on clinical studies, a dosage of 1,200-1,800 mg per day is recommended.

Side Effects / Safety:
N-acetylcysteine was well tolerated during clinical studies, with few side effects reported. A small percentage of users appear to notice dermatological issues (rash, itch, and skin allergy) and/or gastrointestinal distress (loose stool, nausea, diarrhea, vomiting). The effects of chronic high dose NAC supplementation are unknown.

Nettle Root Extract

syn. Urtica Dioica

syn. 3,4-divanillyltetrahydrofuran

PERFORMANCE VALIDATION SCORES	
Combined	6
Clinical Support Rating	1
Empirical Evidence Rating	5

Description:

Stinging nettle (urtica dioica) is an herbal plant found in many warmer parts of Europe, North America, Asia, and Africa. One of the plant's most known physical characteristics is the presence of fine hairs that produce strong pain and irritation upon contact with the skin. The plant actually derives its Latin name from the word for burn (urere). The stinging nettle plant itself is not poisonous, and its leaves are used to make a variety of food products. Stinging nettle leaves and roots also have a long history of use in traditional (natural) medicine, dating back many centuries. It has been used as a diuretic, a laxative, an analgesic, a wound salve, and to treat numerous conditions including arthritis, ulcers, asthma, and diabetes.

Modern studies support many of the traditional uses for nettle leaf and root extracts, suggesting they may offer benefits with ailments such as allergies, sinusitis, benign prostate hypertrophy, arthritis, rheumatism, inflammation, high blood pressure, and even hair loss.[474] Of interest to athletic individuals is a property of one of the lignans (3,4-divanillyltetrahydrofuran) found in the roots. It has displayed an extremely high affinity for binding with sex hormone binding globulin (SHBG), a protein that attaches to testosterone and other sex steroids, preventing them from exerting many activities. If this can occur at a significant level in the body with nettle root extract supplementation, it may allow for a higher percentage of free (bioactive) testosterone. While empirical evidence seems to support the use of nettle root extract as a sports nutrition product, further research is needed to validate its potential ergogenic activity in a clinical setting.

Promoted Benefits:

Nettle root extract is promoted to block SHBG, increase free testosterone levels, and support the anabolic effects of this hormone.

Clinical Studies:

The use of nettle root extract as a sport supplement is only supported by in-vitro clinical studies. Its Clinical Support Rating is 1 (1/ 5).

One such study used test tube experiments to examine the binding of six lignans from the stinging nettle root to SHBG.[475] Five of these lignans (neoolivil, secoisolariciresinol, dehydrodiconiferyl alcohol, isolariciresinol, and 3,4-divanillyltetrahydrofuran) were shown to bind the SHBG protein. The lignan 3,4-divanillyltetrahydrofuran bound SHBG with especially high affinity. Many nettle root extracts are now standardized for this lignan as a result of this data. The researchers also reported SHBG binding activity in two of the most common intestinal metabolites of plant lignans (enterodiol and enterolactone), though their binding was not as pronounced as 3,4-divanillyltetrahydrofuran.

There was a large placebo-controlled study (620 subjects) that examined the effect of nettle root extract in patients with benign prostate hyperplasia, which included measurements of the testosterone level.[476] The study used a dosage of 360 mg/day, which was taken for six months before hormone levels were assayed. The supplementation of nettle root extract did not result in any change in testosterone level compared to placebo. Unfortunately the measure of free testosterone was not taken, so it is unknown if there was a substantial change in the fraction of bioactive testosterone.

Further research is needed to verify if there is ergogenic value to the use of nettle root extract by athletic individuals.

Empirical Evidence:

Nettle root extract is widely available as a stand-alone nutritional supplement. The feedback on this extract for sports nutrition use has been positive, especially with the use of extracts that are standardized for 3,4-divanillyltetrahydrofuran. The primary application in this context is the elevation of endogenous free testosterone levels, and an increase of its anabolic activity. Most users taking these extracts report subjective feelings of elevated androgenicity, and outward signs that the extract is providing the desired effect (oily skin, acne, increased strength). Although there is a lack of substantial clinical support, nettle root extracts do seem to be well regarded among bodybuilders and strength athletes. As with all supplements, however, the effects vary from person to person. Some users do fail to notice positive changes in body composition

or sports performance. Whether this is the result of varying extract potencies, different contexts in which nettle root may impart an ergogenic effect, or individual insensitivity to 3,4-divanillyltetrahydrofuran remains unclear. Nettle root extract (standardized for 3,4-divanillyltetrahydrofuran) has an Empirical Evidence Rating of 5 (5/5).

Effective Dosage:

An effective dosage has not been established. Extracts of varying potencies, and even purified 3,4-divanillyltetrahydrofuran, are available on the sports nutrition market, making dosing difficult to estimate. Manufacturers of standard nettle root extracts commonly recommend 500-1,000 mg per day.

Side Effects / Safety:

Nettle root extract has been well tolerated during clinical studies, with no significant side effects.

Phosphatidylserine

syn. 1,2-diacyl-sn-glycerol 3-phospho-L-serine
syn. 3-O-sn-phosphatidyl-L-serine

PERFORMANCE VALIDATION SCORES

Combined	8
Clinical Support Rating	4
Empirical Evidence Rating	4

Description:

Phosphatidylserine (PS) is a natural phosphate-containing lipid molecule (phospholipid). Phospholipids are a broad class of molecules essential to the structure and function of all cells. Phosphatidylserine is mainly located in the cellular membrane, and concentrated in certain tissues including skeletal muscle. This specific phospholipid is responsible for many important cellular functions including the maintenance of membrane fluidity, the support of receptor concentrations and signaling, and the activity of secondary messengers. The relative concentration of phosphatidylserine next to other phospholipids can help determine cell (and whole organism) physiology.

Phosphatidylserine is widely available as a supplement, typically as a soy-derived product. In addition to its general role in cell functioning, this phospholipid may have several biological activities that are closely tied to athletic performance.[477] For example, phosphatidylserine may reduce the level of serum cortisol, a catabolic hormone. This may help foster an environment that is more favorable for the preservation or synthesis of muscle tissue, as opposed to its breakdown. Phosphatidylserine may also reduce muscle fatigue, increase the time to exhaustion, and improve the rate of recovery after intense exercise. Although more research is needed, there is significant support for these applications of PS, both clinically and empirically.

Promoted Benefits:

Phosphatidylserine is promoted to reduce fatigue, improve muscle recovery after exercise, lower cortisol levels, and support overall muscle growth and athletic performance.

Clinical Studies:

This ingredient has been shown to improve performance in placebo-controlled studies with untrained adults. It has a Clinical Support Rating of 4 (4/5).

With regard to hormone modulation, we can reference a placebo-controlled study that examined the effect of phosphatidylserine on testosterone, growth hormone, lactate, and cortisol levels following exercise in a group of healthy men.[478] Each subject consumed a 600 mg dosage of phosphatidylserine before a 15-minute bout of cycle exercise at moderate intensity (65-85% maximum oxygen consumption). The supplementation of phosphatidylserine was shown to reduce peak cortisol levels (-39%), and improve the extended testosterone to cortisol ratio (+184%), compared to placebo. This study is in agreement with the findings of an earlier investigation showing post-exercise cortisol suppression (-30%) following 10 days of phosphatidylserine supplementation (800 mg/day).[479]

With regard to exercise performance, one placebo-controlled study examined the effects of 10 days of phosphatidylserine supplementation in a group of recreationally active men.[480] Subjects were given a dosage of 750 mg per day. Testing of exercise capacity was conducted on a stationary cycle ergometer, and involved three 10-minute stages at 45%, 55%, and 65% maximum oxygen consumption (VO2max), followed by a bout to exhaustion at 85% VO2max. Phosphatidylserine improved time to exhaustion at 85% VO2max by approximately 30% (7:51 to 9:51), while the placebo had no significant effect.

A second placebo-controlled study examined the effect of 10-days of phosphatidylserine supplementation (750 mg/day) on exercise performance, hormone levels, and markers of muscle damage after intermittent (exhaustive) running in a group of experienced male soccer players.[481] While the study failed to find statistically significant improvements in cortisol levels or markers of muscle damage following phosphatidylserine supplementation, there was a statistically strong trend of improvement in time to exhaustion (+4.2%), suggesting a performance-enhancing benefit.

Another placebo-controlled study looked at the effects of phosphatidylserine on markers of muscle damage after endurance exercise in a group of trained male runners.[482] Subjects consumed either 300 mg or 600 mg of PS per day for a period of 15 days. On the last day of supplementation, the men performed a 90-minute endurance run. Blood was sampled 24 hours later, and compared to baseline measurements. Phosphatidylserine supplementation significantly reduced

levels of creatine kinase (an indicator of muscle damage) compared to placebo. Both dosage levels appeared to have equal efficacy.

An additional placebo-controlled study looked at the effect of phosphatidylserine supplementation on hormone levels and perceived soreness in a group of experienced weightlifters.[483] The dosage taken was 800 mg per day, which was administered for a period of two weeks. During this time the men were subject to a rigorous resistance-training program designed to over train and stress the body. The study demonstrated significant improvements with regard to muscle soreness and perceived sense of wellbeing in subjects taking PS.

Although not all studies are in agreement, there is significant support for the use of phosphatidylserine as an ergogenic supplement.

Empirical Evidence:

Phosphatidylserine has been widely used as a stand-alone supplement. The feedback on this product has generally been positive. Most users report enhanced muscle/exercise endurance, and reduced levels of soreness, with regular supplementation. This is often accompanied by an improved mental state and focus during training. The gains are typically not dramatic, but noticeable nonetheless. A smaller number of users do report dissatisfaction with phosphatidylserine. Given this high cost of this supplement, however, it can be speculated that in some cases this is due to insufficient dosing. Whether a percentage of individuals have a true insensitivity to the performance-enhancing effects of PS supplementation remains unclear. Phosphatidylserine has an Empirical Evidence Rating of 4 (4/5).

Effective Dosage:

Based on clinical studies, a dosage of 300-800 mg daily is recommended.

Side Effects / Safety:

Phosphatidylserine was well tolerated during clinical studies with healthy subjects, with no significant side effects.

Ribose

syn. D-ribose

syn. 5-(hydroxymethyl)oxolane-2,3,4-triol

PERFORMANCE VALIDATION SCORES	
Combined	7
Clinical Support Rating	5
Empirical Evidence Rating	2

Description:

Ribose is a naturally occurring monosaccharide. It is specifically classified as a pentose sugar. Ribose is directly involved in the synthesis and function of several important biological components. These include ribonucleic acids, nucleotides, and riboflavin. Ribose is also integral to muscle energy metabolism. It is used in the synthesis of adenosine triphosphate (ATP), the main form of stored energy for living cells.[484] It also appears to positively modulate the production of free radicals during intense exercise. Ribose is widely available as a sport supplement product, where it is typically applied to help replenish ATP after exercise.

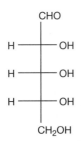

Under normal conditions, the body maintains sufficient levels of ATP. As the muscles reach exhaustion during exercise, however, they may no longer be able to replenish ATP levels fast enough to keep up with its utilization.[485] One study examining a number of different exercise methods found that some reduced ATP levels by nearly 50%.[486] This depletion was associated with impaired recovery of phosphocreatine, reduced pH, and reduced inorganic phosphates. ATP

levels can take many days following intense exercise to fully return to normal, resulting in a prolonged metabolic state that can interfere with optimal performance. Studies examining the effect of ribose on ATP metabolism suggest that it has an especially strong influence on post-exercise ATP replenishment, helping to restore pre-exercise levels more quickly.[487]

The main mode of action for ribose is to play a supportive role in the pentose phosphate pathway. More specifically, it serves as a substrate for the production of phosphoribosyl pyrophosphate (PRPP), an intermediary in the synthesis of ATP. The availability of PRPP is regarded as a rate-limiting step in the ATP energy cycle. This means that its levels are directly tied to those of ATP. Ribose is also found in limited concentrations in skeletal muscle, so an increase in this nutrient can lead to an increase in PRPP, and thus a downstream increase in the availability of ATP. The exact ergogenic value of manipulating ATP concentrations in this manner is still the subject of much research. Under some conditions, however, ribose supplementation may improve exercise capacity and athletic performance.

Promoted Benefits:

Ribose is promoted to increase ATP levels, improve exercise endurance, and enhance athletic performance.

Clinical Studies:

Ribose has been shown to improve performance in placebo-controlled studies with trained adults. It has a Clinical Support Rating of 5 (5/5).

One placebo-controlled study examined the effects of four weeks of ribose supplementation in a group of recreationally active bodybuilders.[488] The subjects took 10 g of ribose per day, and followed a controlled heavy resistance-training program. Muscle strength and endurance were evaluated by assessing bench press 1-rep maximum weight and total repetitions to failure over 10 sets. Subjects taking ribose noticed a statistically significant improvement in bench press 1-rep max (+3.6 kg versus +2.2 kg) and total work (+19.6% versus +12%) compared to placebo. There were no changes in body composition. This study had methodological problems, however, as only five subjects used the supplement (small group size), and the placebo group appeared to be better trained at the beginning (inhomogeneous groups).

A second placebo-controlled study examined the effects of ribose supplementation with high intensity exercise in a group of healthy trained men.[489] The subjects consumed 10 g of ribose per day (5 g twice daily) for five days. Exercise performance was evaluated at baseline and after supplementation by performing two 30-s ergometer cycle sprints under resistance (Wingate anaerobic sprint test). Blood was also sampled for several metabolic markers. While the supplementation of ribose failed to increase peak power, average power, or muscle torque during the Wingate test, or favorably influence ammonia or lactate levels, it did support muscle endurance during the second post-supplementation sprint. Subjects taking placebo noticed a slight decline (-18 J) by this point in the experiment, while performance was maintained with ribose.

Another placebo-controlled study examined the effects of acute ribose supplementation on anaerobic exercise performance in a group of healthy subjects.[490] Participants took 32 g of ribose over a 32-hour window (4 doses of 8 g each). Exercise performance was evaluated before and after supplementation with a series of six 10-second cycle sprints under resistance. The supplementation of ribose produced a statistically significant increase in peak power (+10.9 %) and average power (+6.6%) during sprint number two. Although not statistically significant, there were also strong trends of improvement in peak and average power during sprints number one, number three, and number four in subjects taking ribose.

While the results with ribose are not always positive, studies like these do suggest that its supplementation may improve exercise performance under some conditions, especially with regard to recovery after repeat high intensity activities. Further research is needed to better understand the ergogenic value of ribose.

Empirical Evidence:

Ribose is widely available as a stand-alone nutritional supplement. The feedback on its use as a sport supplement tends to be poor. Some users do appear to notice ergogenic benefit to its use. This is typically centered on a faster rate of recovery following treatment, and a better ability to perform at high level for longer durations (recovery and endurance). The benefits appear to be most noticeable with athletes and bodybuilders who are very in tune with their bodies and personal performance limits, and thus better able to notice minor changes. A stronger strong percentage of users, however, fails to attribute any significant benefit to the use of ribose. It is unknown if this is due to unrealistic expectations, the influence of training or dietary factors, or individual insensitivity to this supplement. Ribose has an Empirical Evidence Rating of 2 (2/5).

Effective Dosage:

Based on clinical studies, a dosage of 10-32 g per day is recommended. Ribose is typically taken with carbohydrates to avoid hypoglycemia.

Side Effects / Safety:

Ribose was well tolerated during clinical studies, with only minor reports of side effects.[491] A small percentage of users do appear to notice gastrointestinal distress (loose stool, nausea, diarrhea) with its use. This appears to be more pronounced with higher doses. Ribose can also produce a hypoglycemic (blood sugar lowering) effect. It is most often consumed with carbohydrates to avoid a significant reduction in blood glucose.

Steroidal Sapogenins

syn. diosgenin and analogs
syn. 25R-spirostanes

PERFORMANCE VALIDATION SCORES	
Combined	1
Clinical Support Rating	1
Empirical Evidence Rating	--

Description:

Steroidal sapogenins (also known as steroidal glycosides) are a group of natural steroid-like molecules widely found in plants. These compounds share the same basic 4-ring carbon skeleton as human steroid hormones such as progesterone, testosterone, estrogen, and cortisol. Because of this, sapogenins are used as starting materials in the synthesis of virtually all steroid medications including synthetic estrogens, progestins, corticosteroids, and anabolic/androgenic steroids.[492] A small number of steroidal sapogenins have also been shown to exhibit weak hormonal activity during in-vitro and in-vivo animal studies (usually estrogenic), although such properties are generally poorly characterized and understood.

In nature, sapogenins are commonly attached to sugars to form a series of soap-like molecules called saponins. Saponins have been shown to possess a wide range of biological activity in mammals.[493, 494] For example, some bind with cholesterol in the bile, inhibiting its reabsorption (reducing serum cholesterol levels). This may potentially allow some to offer a cardio-protective effect. Others have been shown to possess blood thinning, cancer fighting, liver protecting, blood sugar lowering, immune system modulating, neuroprotective, anti-inflammatory, and antioxidant properties. The beneficial properties of saponins are the subject of ongoing research.

Saponins are only partially hydrolyzed to free sapogenins and component sugars during the digestive process.[495] The disassociation of the steroidal sapogenin from its sugar attachment may, therefore, increase or decrease some or all of its various individual biological activities. In some cases, the biological effect may be entirely dependent on retention of the intact saponin molecule.[496] We, therefore, cannot automatically ascribe the beneficial/therapeutic properties of a saponin to its base sapogenin. Each sapogenin must be individually studied, and its properties determined.

Diosgenin (25R-spirost-5-ene-3β,-ol) is the most widely known and studied steroidal sapogenin. It has been shown to exhibit bile acid and cholesterol lowering effects, and may have antioxidant and anti-carcinogenic (cancer fighting) properties.[497, 498] It also appears to exert weak steroid (estrogenic) activity in humans,[499] and has been used as a natural medicine to help alleviate the symptoms of low estrogen associated with menopause.[500] Diosgenin, extracted from the Mexican yam, was the first sapogenin widely used to manufacture steroid drugs. This sapogenin (as well as its source materials such as smilax and Mexican yam) has also been widely sold as a sport nutrition product due to this association. No anabolic action has ever been documented in human studies with diosgenin, however, and it appears unlikely to offer direct ergogenic value.

Several other steroidal sapogenins are also available on the sports nutrition market. What is known of these compounds is summarized below. In most cases these compounds have been linked by their manufacturers to a single Russian study from 1976, which reported strong anabolic (without androgenic) activity in rats given 6-keto derivatives of diosgenin, agigenin, and alliogenin.[501] Although an exact identification of all commercial sapogenins cannot be made due to errors in labeling, it is clear that most (if not all) were never directly mentioned in this original Russian paper. Furthermore, none have been examined in human exercise studies, and clear anabolic, androgenic, or ergogenic effects have not yet been demonstrated.

25(R)-spirost-4-ene-3,6β-diol

This compound is a 4-ene, 6-hydroxyl derivative of diosgenin. At present, the properties of this compound in humans are unknown.

25(R)-spirost-4-ene-3β-ol-6-one

Of the listed saponins, this would be the closest (structurally) to a 6-keto derivative of diosgenin. The exact properties of this compound in humans are unknown. Note that 6-keto diosgenin itself is not possible to synthesize, as its 5-ene group occupies a bond necessary for 6-ketone reduction.

25(R)-5α-spirostan-3β,6α-diol

The compound 25(R)-5alpha-spirostan-3β,6α-diol is a derivative of a sapogenin known as agigenin. It is also commonly referred to as 6alpha-hydroxydiosgenin. The exact properties of this specific sapogenin in humans are unknown.

25(R)-5α-spirostan-3,6-dione

This is a "dione" version of the sapogenin listed above. The exact properties of this compound in humans are also unknown.

Promoted Benefits:

Steroidal sapogenins are promoted to exert anabolic steroid-like activity, increasing muscle mass and strength.

Clinical Studies:

The use of steroidal sapogenins as sport supplements is supported by in-vitro data only. These supplements have a Clinical Support Rating of 1 (1/5).

One in-vitro study demonstrated dioscin (the saponin form of the sapogenin diosgenin) to increase growth hormone secretion when incubated with rat pituitary cells.[502] It is unknown if this effect is retained in diosgenin, or if this compound has growth hormone stimulating or ergogenic effect in exercising humans.

The most commonly cited study on steroidal sapogenins (referenced earlier) was published in 1976, and reported anabolic activity in rats given 6-keto derivatives of the sapogenins agigenin, diosgenin and alliogenin.[503] The most active sapogenin in this study (a 6-keto derivative of alliogenin) produced a significant increase in the weight of rat muscle and organ tissue (heart, liver, and kidney). No significant androgenic effect was seen. It is unknown if this translates into a potential anabolic effect in humans.

Further research is needed to determine if any of the individual steroidal sapogenins have ergogenic effects in humans.

Empirical Evidence:

Steroidal sapogenins are not readily available as stand-alone nutritional supplements. In virtually all sports nutrition products that contain them, they are complexed with other potential ergogenic compounds. This means that even an anecdotal assessment of their individual anabolic or performance-enhancing properties is very difficult to make. Many

researchers in the field (including myself) are re-
served about the potential anabolic action of these
steroid-like plant compounds, but do recommend further research. An Empirical Evidence Rating is
presently unavailable for steroidal sapogenins.

Effective Dosage:

Effective dosages for these supplement compounds
have not been established.

Side Effects / Safety:

Diosgenin appears to be well tolerated, with few side
effects reported.[504] None of the other cited sapogenins
has been the subject of peer-reviewed human safety
evaluations.

Sulfo-Polysaccharide Extract

syn. cystoseira canariensis

Description:

This sport supplement consists of a concentrated blend of natural sulfated polysaccharides that have been extracted from brown seaweed (specifically the species cystoseira canariensis). Brown seaweed extracts like this have been shown to possess a number of biological activities in humans, the most widely studied of which are antioxidant and anti-viral. This particular extract has been heavily promoted to inhibit the human myostatin protein, a negative regulator of muscle growth. By binding this protein, it has been stated that sulfo-polysaccharide extract can support an increase in skeletal muscle mass and strength.

Sulfo-polysaccharide extract was first released as a sport supplement in 2002. Around this time, myostatin had been the subject of much scientific research and discussion. In particular, it was shown that inhibiting myostatin in certain animals (such as mice and bulls) caused them to develop enormous amounts of muscle mass compared to those with a normally functioning protein. Naturally, a dietary supplement that could inhibit the myostatin protein garnered a great deal of public interest. Unfortunately, this supplement did not appear to have the stated physiological effect. Recent studies have suggested that sulfo-polysaccharide extract does not have any myostatin-inhibiting or performance-enhancing effect, and the original manufacturer has since abandoned this supplement. It may remain available through other suppliers.

Promoted Benefits:

Sulfo-polysaccharide extract is promoted to inhibit myostatin and increase muscle mass and strength.

Clinical Studies:

The use of sulfo-polysaccharide extract as a sport supplement is only supported by one in-vitro clinical study. Its Clinical Support Rating is 1 (1/ 5).

The one potentially supportive study that was published on sulfo-polysaccharide extract involved its incubation in serum with the myostatin protein.[505] The investigators reported that sulfo-polysaccharide extract was able to bind myostatin. This is a preliminary investigation only, and may not relate to any bioactive effect in humans supplementing this extract.

There have been two additional placebo-controlled studies examining the effects of sulfo-polysaccharide extract on exercising adults. Neither study supports the use of sulfo-polysaccharide extract as a sport supplement.

The first study examined the supplementation of 1,200 mg/day for 12 weeks in a group of resistance-trained men.[506] The study did not find any significant difference between supplement and placebo groups with regard to total body mass, fat-free mass, muscle strength, or thigh volume/mass. Furthermore, an examination of serum myostatin showed that sulfo-polysaccharide extract did not inhibit this protein.

The second study involved the supplementation of sulfo-polysaccharide extract for eight weeks (500 mg/day) in a group of men with resistance-training experience.[507] Investigators could not find any statistically significant or strong trends of improvement caused by sulfo-polysaccharide extract in any marker of performance, anabolic/catabolic status, or body composition.

Empirical Evidence:

Sulfo-polysaccharide extract has been widely used as a stand-alone supplement. Given the high interest in myostatin at the time this ingredient was released to market, many consumers had strong expectations for it. Unfortunately, individual experiences did not live up to these expectations. A strong majority of people reported that they did not notice any benefit with regard to muscle mass or strength from the supplement. Only a small number of users seemed to report that a positive response might have occurred, which may simply be due to placebo effect. Sulfo-polysaccharide extract has an Empirical Evidence Rating of 1 (1/5).

Effective Dosage:

An effective dosage of this supplement has not been established. Manufacturers commonly recommend 1,000-2,000 mg per day.

Side Effects / Safety:

Sulfo-polysaccharide was well tolerated during clinical studies, with no reported side effects.

Tribulus Terrestris

syn. puncturevine
syn. Bai Ji Li

PERFORMANCE VALIDATION SCORES	
Combined	6
Clinical Support Rating	2
Empirical Evidence Rating	4

Description:

Tribulus terrestris is an herbal plant native to many temperate regions of the world. It has a history of use in traditional Chinese and Indian (Ayurvedic) medicine that dates back centuries. Tribulus terrestris has also been widely used in Eastern Europe, and in the early 1980's was introduced as a medicinal product in Bulgaria. Tribulus is mainly applied as an aphrodisiac, to treat erectile dysfunction, and as a general tonic for improving vitality and energy in older men. More recently, extracts of this plant have been popularly marketed to bodybuilders, claiming that the herb can increase testosterone levels and facilitate the anabolic effects of this hormone.

Modern studies with animals do confirm libido stimulating and erection supporting properties of this traditional herbal medicine.[508,509] The exact mechanism that imparts such action, however, remains unclear. Studies on several animal species have demonstrated a notable ability to increase serum androgen (testosterone, DHT) levels.[510] Thus far, however, human studies have failed to demonstrate the same. Whether this is due to individual variances, study methodological difficulties, or a true absence of consistent hormone elevating effect remains unclear. Further study is needed to determine what, if any, influence tribulus terrestris has over human male androgenicity. It is also presently unknown if tribulus terrestris extract has tangible ergogenic value.

The main biologically active component in tribulus terrestris is believed to be a steroidal saponin named protodioscin. Numerous additional saponins have also been identified in this plant, however, including prototribestin, pseudoprotodioscin, dioscin, tribestin, and tribulosin.[511] Steroidal saponins share the basic 4-carbon ring skeleton of all steroids, but not necessarily inherent androgen-, estrogen-, cortisol-, or progesterone-like activity. A full understanding of each saponin has not been achieved, and thus the activity of tribulus remains the subject of much speculation. Sport supplements containing tribulus terrestris extract are typically standardized for protodioscin or total steroidal saponin content.

Promoted Benefits:

Tribulus terrestris extract is promoted to increase testosterone levels, and support muscle mass and strength gains.

Clinical Studies:

The use of tribulus terrestris as a sport supplement is supported by animal data only. Its Clinical Support Rating is 2 (2/5).

Data provided from Sopharma, the Bulgarian manufacturer of medicinal tribulus terrestris (Tribeston), is widely referenced to demonstrate the testosterone elevating properties of this plant extract. This internal study ostensibly demonstrates a weak but positive effect on male hormones.[512] This study, however, was

137

not placebo-controlled nor independently reviewed and published. It therefore cannot be accepted as clinical validation.

The most commonly cited independent study demonstrating a positive effect on anabolic hormone levels involved the administration of various doses (2.5-30 mg/kg of body weight) of the extract orally or intravenously to rabbits, rats, and primates.[513] The administration period lasted for up to eight weeks. All animals noticed increases in androgen levels (testosterone, DHT) ranging from 25-52%. The increase in rats was 25% after oral doses of 5 mg/kg of body weight.

A placebo-controlled study with a group of healthy young men failed to find a similar increase in serum testosterone levels.[514] It involved administering tribulus terrestris extract at a dose of 10 mg/kg or 20 mg/kg of body weight daily for a period of four weeks. Hormonal measures were taken at various points during the experiment. The study did not find any statistically significant effect of tribulus terrestris on serum androgen levels.

An additional placebo-controlled study examined the effects of tribulus terrestris extract on muscle strength and body composition in a group of elite rugby players.[515] Subjects consumed 450 mg per day of the extract during a five-week period of intense resistance training. The study found no difference between the supplement and placebo groups with regard to body composition (lean body mass) or strength.

Another placebo-controlled study was conducted with a group of resistance-trained men.[516] Subjects consumed 3.21 mg/kg of body weight of tribulus terrestris extract daily for eight weeks, and underwent a controlled resistance-training program. The study demonstrated no changes in muscle mass, strength,

total body water, or calorie intake as a result of tribulus terrestris supplementation.

Further research is needed to determine if tribulus terrestris can be used to increase male androgen levels, and if there is any ergogenic value to its application by athletic individuals.

Empirical Evidence:
Tribulus terrestris extract has been widely used as a stand-alone supplement. The feedback on this supplement has been somewhat positive. A good percentage of users report subjective feelings of increased androgenicity (increased vitality, energy, libido, and training aggressiveness). Some are even able to associate this with a tangible increase in muscle mass and strength. Such strong results, however, are very inconsistent. A fair percentage of users are unable to attribute any specific benefit to tribulus supplementation, and often report its use is without merit. Tribulus terrestris extract has an Empirical Evidence Rating of 4 (4/5).

Effective Dosage:
An effective dosage of this supplement has not been established. Manufacturers commonly recommend 500-1,500 mg per day.

Side Effects / Safety:
Tribulus terrestris extract was well tolerated during all clinical studies, with no significant side effects.

ZMA (zinc magnesium aspartate)

syn. Zinc, Magnesium, Vitamin B6

PERFORMANCE VALIDATION SCORES	
Combined	4
Clinical Support Rating	0
Empirical Evidence Rating	4

Description:

ZMA, which stands for Zinc Magnesium Aspartate, is a combination vitamin and mineral supplement marketed to athletes and other individuals undergoing rigorous exercise programs. Each serving contains 30 mg of zinc monomethionine aspartate and 450 mg of magnesium aspartate, which are simply bioavailable forms of the minerals zinc and magnesium. Each serving also contains 10.5 mg of vitamin B6. Each vitamin and mineral of this formula is an important essential nutrient for the human body, especially with regard to maintaining optimum energy levels and physical performance.

With regard to those metabolic processes important for athletic activity, we find that zinc is involved in energy metabolism during intense physical exertion. It is also important to the production of testosterone, the primary male anabolic/androgenic sex hormone. Magnesium is necessary for a myriad of cellular and enzymatic functions, including glycogen breakdown, protein synthesis, lipolysis (body fat breakdown), and ATP replenishment. Vitamin B6 is important for optimal protein metabolism, and is also necessary for maximum muscle and liver glycogen storage. A deficiency in any one of these nutrients could, likewise, significantly impair athletic performance.

Athletic individuals may have higher requirements for these three nutrients than sedentary (non-exercising) individuals. High levels of activity have been shown to produce increases in urinary minerals, for example. Sweating is also increased with intense exertion, and is another conduit for the loss of key minerals. Already, many Americans have diets that are not sufficient in these vitamins and minerals. Studies further suggest that supplementing zinc, magnesium, or vitamin B6, at least to correct deficiencies, can improve exercise performance.[517,518] Beyond the simple supplementation of zinc, magnesium, and B6 with any sufficient vitamin/mineral product, however, there is no data that presently supports a unique role of the ZMA formula in improving athletic performance.

Promoted Benefits:

ZMA is promoted to elevate testosterone and IGF-1 levels and improve athletic performance.

Clinical Studies:

The specific ZMA vitamin/mineral blend is not supported by any independent clinical studies suggesting efficacy as a sport supplement. It has a Clinical Support Rating of 0 (0/5).

The most widely cited placebo-controlled study with regard to ZMA involved its supplementation by a group of NCAA Division II college football athletes for eight weeks.[519] The study demonstrated statistically significant improvements in serum free testosterone (+33%) and muscle strength (+11%). Although detailed, this study cannot be accepted as independent validation, as it was conducted and authored in part by the inventor of the ZMA formula.

There have been two independent placebo-controlled investigations into the use of the ZMA with exercising adults. Neither study supports this formula as a sport supplement.

The first study involved the administration of ZMA for eight weeks to a group of young men that exercised regularly.[520] All of the subjects had their diets analyzed for zinc content, and none were considered deficient. Pre- and post-supplementation zinc levels were shown to be similar to those of the subjects in the Conte study. This study demonstrated no change in either the serum total or free testosterone level as a result of supplementation.

The second study examined the effects of a ZMA supplement in a group of resistance-trained men.[521] The participants took the product for eight weeks, during which time they were subject to a standardized resistance-training program and examined for changes in serum anabolic hormone levels (testosterone, IGF-1), body composition, and markers of anaerobic performance. The ZMA supplemented subjects did not notice any improvements compared to those taking placebo.

These studies suggest that while zinc, magnesium, and vitamin B6 supplementation might improve exercise performance when used to correct a dietary deficiency, the use of ZMA by individuals with a sufficient dietary intake may not offer further improvements in anabolic hormone status, body composition, or athletic performance.

Empirical Evidence:

Zinc Magnesium Asparate is widely available as a stand-alone supplement. The feedback on this vitamin/mineral formula has been somewhat positive. A good percentage of users do seem to report finding some value in this supplement. Given the fact that many Americans fail to consume enough of these micronutrients, and athletes may have heightened needs for them, ZMA may be serving to correct a deficiency in many of these cases. A standard vitamin and mineral supplement, however, should also accomplish the same thing. A good percentage of users do not report any improvements after adding ZMA to their regular exercise/supplementation routines. Given the results of recent clinical studies, it seems plausible that many of these individuals have diets that are sufficient in these nutrients, and therefore would not notice the exercise improvements that come with correcting deficiency. ZMA has an Empirical Evidence Rating of 4 (4/5).

Effective Dosage:

An efficacious dose of the ZMA vitamin/mineral blend has not been established.

Side Effects / Safety:

Zinc, magnesium, and vitamin B6 are essential micronutrients. Unless they are taken in excess, they should not present any significant side effects.

Consumer Empowerment

Rules for Effective Shopping

Now that you understand the ingredients and just how the business of sports nutrition works, you should be much better prepared to make the most out of your hard-earned money. To that point, I have assembled five simple rules to remember when shopping. I strongly suggest you follow them any time you plan on spending significant money on performance-enhancing supplements. It may take a little work to follow these rules, as they require figuring out on your own what you need to meet your goals. But I assure you, the time it takes to make up your own program will be well worth it in the long run. Once you know what you are looking for, you are the one calling the shots. All the celebrity endorsements, fancy boxes, and outrageous advertising claims melt away. What is left is an honest assessment of a supplement's worth, and your interest (or not) in using it.

Rule #1: Ignore marketing claims
Advertising tends to come from the marketing department, not the laboratory. The people that write the copy for these companies are generally not scientists, but creative writers and advertising executives. You are better off ignoring all marketing claims. Look only at what is substantial about the product, not what an ad-copy writer wants you to think so that you will buy it.

Rule #2: Look at ingredients and dosages only
Most companies make their products by finding one or two commodity ingredients to work with, and blending them up with many other components to make the formula look good. The more ingredients and the less information they give you, the harder it is to determine the value of what you are buying (and likely the more money they can charge for it). You should look at two things on the label above all else. Look to see what ingredients are in the product, and then in what dosages are they used. Nothing else on the label matters.

Rule #3: Make a list
You should already be looking for specific ingredients when you begin your shopping. List them before you visit the store. Design your supplement program first, and find the products to fit it. Also remember that you are very likely to spend much less buying a few individual single-ingredient products, than looking for fancy multi-ingredient formulas that have everything you are looking for in one.

Rule #4: Try individual ingredients first
The response to supplementation can be a very individual thing. What works extremely well for some people may not work the same way for you. There is no use continuing to spend money on something that doesn't work the way you need it to. The best way to avoid this is to try each key sport supplement individually before you build combination programs using them. This will give you a chance to learn exactly how your body responds to a particular ingredient. Use it for a good amount of time so you are sure (several weeks at a minimum). Once you discover those basic products that you respond very well to, you are then in a much better position to organize supplementation programs that make use of several products at once (without wondering what is, and is not, helping).

Rule #5: Find companies you can trust
Sports nutrition is a very large industry. There are many companies to choose from when shopping. As we have discussed, there are many companies with good reputations and products of high value. There are also many companies much more focused on their margins than your results. Generally, companies are fairly consistent with how they handle themselves.

Once you've familiarized yourself with the market, and have discovered those companies with good reputations and products that meet your needs, try to stick with them. The better companies take customer loyalty very seriously, and will undoubtedly be trying to retain your business.

Top Rated Supplements (Quick Reference)

This section provides a quick reference of those supplements with the highest combined clinical and empirical validation rating (7 or higher). They represent the products that should offer you the highest chance of success. It is important to emphasize that these are not necessarily the only effective products in sports nutrition. As discussed already, this is a field of innovation, and there are always new technologies. There may very well be other ingredients that are on the path to becoming established ergogenic aids. As it stands right now, however, these are the most proven sport supplements. Given that groundbreaking products of tangible value do not come out very often, focusing on these ingredients (instead of chasing the latest hyped-up supplement releases) should provide the strongest foundation on which to make progress.

Weightlifting (Size, Strength)

These are the top rated anabolic supplements, most likely to help you increase muscle size and strength when taken in conjunction with intense resistance training.

Supplement	Daily Amount
Adenosine triphosphate (ATP)	100-250 mg
Alpha-Lipoic Acid (ALA)	600-1,800 mg
Androst-4-ene,3,6,17-trione (6-OXO)	300-600 mg
Arachidonic Acid (ARA)	400-1,000 mg
Arginine	3-9 grams
Arginine Alpha-Ketoglutarate (AAKG)	12 grams
Beta-Alanine	3-6 grams
Branched-Chain Amino Acids (BCAA)	5-20 grams
Conjugated-Linoleic Acid (CLA)	5-6 grams
Creatine	3-5 grams
Glutamine	10-30 grams
HMB (beta-hydroxy-beta-methylbutyrate)	3 grams
Leucine	3-10 grams
Longjack	100-200 mg

Sports Performance (Energy, Power, Anaerobic Endurance)

These supplements should allow you to perform for a longer period of time at optimal levels in sporting activities where brief repeat high energy output is required. These activities may include baseball, football, sprinting, long jumping, swimming, etc.

Supplement	Daily Amount
Adenosine triphosphate (ATP)	100-250 mg
Arachidonic Acid (ARA)	400-1,000 mg
Alpha-Glycerylphosphorylcholine	600-1,200 mg
Alpha-Lipoic Acid (ALA)	600-1,800 mg
Beta-alanine	3-6 grams
Betaine	2.5 grams
Branched-Chain Amino Acids (BCAA)	5-20 grams
Caffeine	<400 mg
Carnitine	2-4 grams
Citrulline malate	6 grams
Creatine	3-5 grams
Glutamine	10-30 grams
Glycine-Arginine-Alpha-Ketoisocaproic Acid (GAAKA)	11.2 grams
Glycine Propionyl-L-Carnitine (GPLC)	4.5 grams
HMB (Beta-Hydroxy-Beta-Methylbutyrate)	3 grams
Leucine	3-10 grams
N-Acetylcysteine	1,200-1,800 mg
Phosphatidylserine	300-800 mg
Ribose	10-32 grams

Sports Performance (Aerobic Endurance)

The following supplements are the most likely to improve performance during prolonged endurance (aerobic) activities, such as running, jogging, and cycling.

Supplement	Daily Amount
Adenosine triphosphate (ATP)	100-250 mg
Beta-alanine	3-6 grams
Betaine	2.5 grams
Branched-Chain Amino Acids (BCAA)	5-20 grams
Caffeine	<400 mg
Carnitine	2-4 grams
Citrulline malate	6 grams
Fish oil (EPA/DHA)	3-6 grams
Leucine	3-10 grams
N-Acetylcysteine	1,200-1,800 mg
Phosphatidylserine	300-800 mg

Sample Supplement Programs

The first step to effective supplementation should be familiarizing yourself with the effects of each key ergogen in your respective class of activity. Once you have a better idea of what works well for you individually, you will probably start thinking about ways to combine these supplements. This section addresses this issue by detailing several sample multi-supplement programs for improving bodybuilding and sports performance. They represent some of the most basic and/or effective regimens, but are by no means the only effective way of using these supplements. It is important to emphasize that sports nutrition is a very individualized thing. The particular dietary and supplementation needs of any one athlete can be very different from others, even in the same sport. These programs, therefore, are meant only to serve as a starting point for the development of your own individually tailored programs.

Weightlifting/Bodybuilding: Program #1 (8-12 Weeks)

Daily:

Creatine   5 grams (plus 5 days loading at 20 grams)

Beta-Alanine   3-6 grams

Pre- or During-Training:

High GI carbohydrates (30 grams)

Post-Training:

High GI carbohydrates (50-100 grams)

Whey Protein 25-50 grams

Comments:

This is one of the most basic and cost-effective supplement programs for bodybuilding. Beta-alanine is known to augment the muscle-building effects of creatine, and like creatine also increases muscle power and endurance, but through a different and complimentary mechanism (maintenance of muscle pH). While creatine is responsible for increasing intracellular water retention, there is usually a significant retention of weight and lean muscle mass at the conclusion of this program. This program would be highly recommended for someone not wishing to invest a great deal of money, yet still looking for a strong anabolic effect.

Weightlifting/Bodybuilding: Program #2 (7 Weeks)

Daily:

Arachidonic Acid   750-1,000 mg

Androst-4-ene,3,6,17-trione (6-OXO)   300-600 mg

Pre- or During-Training:

High GI carbohydrates (30 grams) + BCAA (10 grams)

Post-Training:

High GI carbohydrates (50-100 grams) + BCAA (10 grams)

Whey Protein 25-50 grams

Comments:

This is another highly effective supplement combination for increasing lean body mass. 6-OXO and arachidonic acid display a good synergy with each other, the first increasing testosterone levels, and the latter tissue sensitivity to anabolic hormones. The added BCAAs further help to reduce muscle protein catabolism and increase synthesis. This program is going to be more expensive than the creatine + beta alanine stack, although it may provide more substantial results. If 6-OXO is unavailable, Longjack (200 mg/day) could be used, although it may not be an equal replacement (it is not as effective at raising testosterone levels). Because this program includes a testosterone booster, it is for men only.

Weightlifting/Bodybuilding: Program #3 (8-12 Weeks)

Daily:

Creatine   5 grams (plus 5 days loading at 20 grams)

Arginine Alpha-Ketoglutarate (AAKG)   12 grams

Pre- or During-Training:

High GI carbohydrates (30 grams) + BCAA (10 grams)

Post-Training:

High GI carbohydrates (50-100 grams) + BCAA (10 grams)

Whey Protein 25-50 grams

Comments:

Creatine plus arginine is also considered a very basic and fundamental supplement stack. Arginine alpha-ketoglutarate is preferred, as it appears to be more solidly supported as an ergogen in the medical literature. This combination seems to work extremely well for almost all users, barring a small percentage of individuals who are non-responsive to creatine. Some or the entire creatine dose should be taken in the post-exercise recovery window on training days.

Weightlifting/Bodybuilding: Program #4 (8 Weeks)

Daily:

HMB (beta-hydroxy-beta-methylbutyrate)   3 grams

Arginine Alpha-Ketoglutarate (AAKG)   12 grams

Pre- or During-Training:

High GI carbohydrates (30 grams) + BCAA (10 grams)

Post-Training:

High GI carbohydrates (50-100 grams) + BCAA (10 grams)

Whey Protein 25-50 grams

Comments:

This is a commonly recommended stack for those getting introduced to sports nutrition. This stack seems to elicit mixed results, although I think enough people perform well enough with it that it is worth mentioning. For HMB/arginine responsive individuals, it seems to produce a fair gain in lean mass along with a good increase in strength, and strong vasodilation (pump) during training.

Weightlifting/Bodybuilding: Program #5 (8-12 Weeks)

Daily:

Beta-Alanine   3-6 grams

Conjugated-Linoleic Acid (CLA)   5 grams

Creatine   5 grams (plus 5 days loading at 20 grams)

Pre- or During-Training:

High GI carbohydrates (30 grams) + BCAA (10 grams)

Post-Training:

High GI carbohydrates (50-100 grams) + BCAA (10 grams)

Whey Protein 25-50 grams

Comments:

This is a expansion of the first supplement program, making use of an additional 5-gram daily dose of CLA to help better partition nutrients to muscle instead of fat storage. BCAA's have also been added to better support protein synthesis and reduce protein catabolism during training.

Weightlifting/Bodybuilding: Program #6 (7 Weeks)

Daily:

Arachidonic Acid   750-1,000 mg

Alpha-Lipoic Acid (ALA)   600 mg

Beta-Alanine   3-6 grams

Pre- or During-Training:

High GI carbohydrates (30 grams) + BCAA (10 grams)

Post-Training:

High GI carbohydrates (50-100 grams) + BCAA (10 grams)

Whey Protein 25-50 grams

Comments:

This is another effective combination for increasing lean body mass. Beta-alanine is extremely effective at aiding muscle endurance, allowing the individual to push more reps and sets during their weight training sessions. Arachidonic acid release from contracting muscle fibers serves as a root trigger in the anabolic process. So you have more physical stimulation on the one hand, yielding even higher levels of ARA release on the other. Alpha-lipoic acid has also been added to help with nutrient delivery in the muscles, which should help with the heightened rates of protein synthesis.

Sports Performance (Anaerobic): Program #1 (12+ weeks)

Daily:

Beta-alanine   3-6 grams

Citrulline malate   6 grams

Pre-Training/Competition:

High GI carbohydrates (30-60 grams)

During Training/Competition:

High GI carbohydrates (30 grams/hr)

Post-Training/Competition:

High GI carbohydrates (50-100 grams)

Whey Protein 25-50 grams

Comments:

Beta-alanine and citrulline malate make an excellent supplement combination for sports activities, especially for those not fond of the extra water weight brought on by creatine supplementation. These two products typically provide a very good boost in muscle endurance, as well as rate of recovery after training and events. The combination is often used for several months, or a competitive season. Given the wide variety of sports, as well as the variability in intensity, duration, and dietary requirements for recovery, the pre- during- and post-training/competition carbohydrate supplementation schedules for all sports programs serve as general guidelines only, and may be adjusted as necessary.

Sports Performance (Anaerobic): Program #2 (8-12 Weeks)

Daily:

Alpha-Glycerylphosphorylcholine   600-1,200 mg

Phosphatidylserine   300-800 mg

Pre-Training/Competition:

High GI carbohydrates (30-60 grams)

Caffeine 3 mg/kg (bodyweight)

During Training/Competition:

High GI carbohydrates (30 grams/hr)

Post-Training/Competition:

High GI carbohydrates (50-100 grams)

Whey Protein 25-50 grams

Comments:

This program uses Caffeine and Alpha-GPC to support mental focus and energy. Phosphatidylserine is also used to improve muscle endurance and recovery following intense activity. The effect of this program may be slightly subtler that those based on stronger ergogenic substances, but should still provide noticeable improvements in mental and physical performance.

Sports Performance (Anaerobic): Program #3 (8 Weeks)

Daily:

Arachidonic Acid (ARA)   500 mg

Beta-alanine   3-6 grams

Pre-Training/Competition:

High GI carbohydrates (30-60 grams)

During Training/Competition:

High GI carbohydrates (30 grams/hr)

Post-Training/Competition:

High GI carbohydrates (50-100 grams) + BCAA (10 grams)

Whey Protein 25-50 grams

Comments:

This combination focuses on the use of beta-alanine, mainly for its muscle endurance promoting properties, and arachidonic acid for increasing power output during sports. Branched-chain amino acids have also been added to help support muscle recovery after training/competition. Given the inclusion of arachidonic acid, this program is tailored for sports requiring a high output of muscle power, or those where intermittent bursts of energy are required.

Sports Performance (Anaerobic): Program #4 (8-12 Weeks)

Daily:

Ribose 10-32 grams

Creatine   3-5 grams

Pre-Training/Competition:

Glycine-Arginine-Alpha-Ketoisocaproic Acid (GAAKA)   11.2 grams

High GI carbohydrates (30-60 grams)

During Training/Competition:

High GI carbohydrates (30 grams/hr)

Post-Training/Competition:

High GI carbohydrates (50-100 grams)

Whey Protein 25-50 grams

Comments:

This supplement combination should promote increases in energy and endurance during training or sports activities. Creatine does promote intracellular water retention, but generally this does not hinder performance. Creatine, in fact, appears to be very effective for general sports use. GAAKA has also been used in this program as a pre-workout supplement, which is in line with the clinical data on this ingredient so far (showing significant improvements in performance with this method of use). It, however, may also be used daily.

Sports Performance (Aerobic Endurance): Program #1 (8-12 Weeks)

Daily:

Beta-alanine   3-6 grams

Pre-Training/Competition:

Caffeine 3 mg/kg (bodyweight)

High GI carbohydrates (30-60 grams)

During Training/Competition:

Water or High GI carbohydrates (30 grams/hr)

Post-Training/Competition:

High GI carbohydrates (50-100 grams)

Whey Protein 25 grams

Comments:

This program uses beta-alanine as its backbone ergogen, which has been shown to help stabilize pH and extend endurance. Caffeine has been added as a pre-workout supplement to help support energy levels, and is likely most useful if the activity will last for 1 hour or less (such as medium distance running). Carbohydrates are recommended during the activity to further support energy, and preferably should be taken in the form of a sports energy drink with balanced electrolytes.

Sports Performance (Aerobic Endurance): Program #2 (8-12 Weeks)

Daily:

Carnitine   2-4 grams

N-Acetylcysteine   1,200-1,800 mg

Fish oil (EPA/DHA)   3-6 grams

Pre-Training/Competition:

Betaine   2.5 grams

High GI carbohydrates (30-60 grams)

During Training/Competition:

Water or High GI carbohydrates (30 grams/hr)

Post-Training/Competition:

High GI carbohydrates (50-100 grams)

Whey Protein 25 grams

Comments:

This supplement stack focuses on reducing oxidative stress in the muscles, which may interfere with performance and recovery. Carnitine is also used to help promote the utilization of fat for energy during prolonged exercise, which can enhance the production of ATP and further support prolonged exercise endurance.

Sports Performance (Aerobic Endurance): Program #3 (8-12 Weeks)

Daily:

N-Acetylcysteine	1,200-1,800 mg
Phosphatidylserine	300-800 mg

Pre-Training/Competition:

High GI carbohydrates (30-60 grams)

During Training/Competition:

Water or High GI carbohydrates (30 grams/hr)

Post-Training/Competition:

High GI carbohydrates (50-100 grams)

Whey Protein 25 grams

Comments:

The combination of N-acetylcysteine and phosphatidylserine are often highly favored for reducing oxidative stress and promoting muscle recovery after exercise. Both supplements have also been tied to improvements in aerobic exercise performance, and should enhance muscle endurance during prolonged activities.

Sports Performance (Aerobic Endurance): Program #4 (8-12 Weeks)

Daily:

Citrulline malate   6 grams

Pre-Training/Competition:

Betaine   2.5 grams

Adenosine triphosphate (ATP)   100-250 mg

High GI carbohydrates (30-60 grams)

During Training/Competition:

Water or High GI carbohydrates (30 grams/hr)

Post-Training/Competition:

High GI carbohydrates (50-100 grams)

Whey Protein 25 grams

Comments:

This program centers on improving cellular energy production and aerobic exercise endurance. Citrulline malate is the only supplement taken daily, and serves as the backbone ingredient of this program. ATP and betaine are taken shortly before all training sessions and competition events, to provide acute (immediate) improvements in aerobic performance. All supplements could be taken daily as well, if preferred. Note that it may be difficult to find an isolated ATP supplement.

References

1. Is increased dietary protein necessary or beneficial for individuals with a physically active lifestyle? Lemon PW. Nutr Rev. 1996 Apr;54(4 Pt 2):S169-75.

2. Food intake, nitrogen and energy balance in Polish weight lifters, during a training camp. Celejowa I, Homa M. Nutr Metab. 1970;12(5):259-74.

3. Protein requirements and muscle mass/strength changes during intensive training in novice bodybuilders. Lemon PW, Tarnopolsky MA, MacDougall JD, Atkinson SA. J Appl Physiol. 1992 Aug;73(2):767-75.

4. Do regular high protein diets have potential healthy risks on kidney function in athletes? Poortmans J. et al. Int J Sport Nutr Exer Metab 10:28-38 (2000)

5. Slow and fast dietary proteins differently modulate postprandial protein accretion. Yves Boirie et al. Proc. Natl. Acad. Sci. V.94 pp. 14930-35. December, 1997.

6. Valine May Be the First Limiting Branched-Chain Amino Acid in Egg Protein in Men Roya Riazi, Mahroukh Rafii. American Society for Nutritional Sciences J. Nutr. 133:3533-3539, November 2003.

7. A method of determining the biological value of protein. H H. Mitchell. Journal of Biological Chemistry. Received November 19, 1923.

8. Rafalski, H. and Nogal, E. Proceedings of 7th International Congress on Nutrition. 4: 307. Pergamon Press, London (1966).

9. Williams MH. Nutrition for Health, Fitness and Sport. 7th ed. New York: McGraw-Hill 2007.

10. Nutritional needs of elite athletes. Part I: Carbohydrate and fluid requirements. Tarnopolsky MA et al. Eur J Sport Sci 5: 3-14 2005.

11. Mechanisms of muscle fatigue in intense exercise. Green HJ. J Sports Sci. 1997 Jun;15(3):247-56.

12. Glycemic index and glycemic load in relation to changes in body weight, body fat distribution, and body composition in adult Danes. Hare-Bruun H, Flint A, Heitmann BL. Am J Clin Nutr. 2006 Oct;84(4):871-9; quiz 952-3.

13. Glycemic index in chronic disease: a review. Augustin LS, Franceschi S, Jenkins DJ, Kendall CW, La Vecchia C. Eur J Clin Nutr. 2002 Nov;56(11):1049-71. Review.

14. Glycemic index, glycemic load, and chronic disease risk--a meta-analysis of observational studies. Barclay AW, Petocz P, McMillan-Price J, Flood VM, Prvan T, Mitchell P, Brand-Miller JC. Am J Clin Nutr. 2008 Mar;87(3):627-37. Review.

15. Glycemic Index Values takes from BloodIndex.com

16. Effects of pre-exercise ingestion of trehalose, galactose and glucose on subsequent metabolism and cycling performance. R.L.P.G. Jentjens. A.E. Jeukendrup. Eur J Appl Physiol (2003) 88: 459–465

17. What Are Sugar Alcohols? Comparisons and Blood Sugar Impact. Laura Dolson, About.com. Updated: April 13,

2009

18. Pre-exercise carbohydrate and fluid ingestion: influence of glycemic response on 10-km run treadmill running performance in the heat. Mitchell JB et al. J Sports Med Phys Res 40: 41-50 1989.

19. Carbohydrate ingestion can completely suppress endogenous glucose production during exercise. Asker E. Jeukendrup et al. Am J Physiol Endocrinol Metab 276: E672-E683, 1999

20. Determinants of post-exercise glycogen synthesis during short-term recovery. Jentjens R, Jeukendrup A. Sports Med. 2003;33(2):117-44.

21. Muscle glycogen synthesis after exercise: effect of time of carbohydrate ingestion. Ivy JL, Katz AL, Cutler CL, Sherman WM, Coyle EF. J Appl Physiol. 1988 Apr;64(4):1480-5.

22. Muscle glycogen synthesis before and after exercise. - Ivy JL - Sports Med - 01-JAN-1991; 11(1): 6-19

23. Muscle glycogen synthesis after exercise: effect of time of carbohydrate ingestion. Ivy JL, Katz AL, Cutler CL, Sherman WM, Coyle EF. J Appl Physiol. 1988 Apr;64(4):1480-5.

24. Dietary strategies to promote glycogen synthesis after exercise. Ivy JL. Can J Appl Physiol. 2001;26 Suppl:S236-45.

25. Determinants of post-exercise glycogen synthesis during short-term recovery. Jentjens R, Jeukendrup A. Sports Med. 2003;33(2):117-44.

26. Glycogen depletion and increased insulin sensitivity and responsiveness in muscle after exercise. Zorzano A, Balon TW, Goodman MN, Ruderman NB. Am J Physiol. 1986 Dec;251(6 Pt 1):E664-9.

27. Protein supplements and exercise. Wolfe RR. Am J Clin Nutr. 2000 Aug;72(2 Suppl):551S-7S.

28. Intracellular signalling pathways regulating the adaptation of skeletal muscle to exercise and nutritional changes. Matsakas A, Patel K. Histol Histopathol. 2009 Feb;24(2):209-22.

29. Recovery from a cycling time trial is enhanced with carbohydrate-protein supplementation vs. isoenergetic carbohydrate supplementation. Berardi JM, Noreen EE, Lemon PW. J Int Soc Sports Nutr. 2008 Dec 24;5:24.

30. Early postexercise muscle glycogen recovery is enhanced with a carbohydrate-protein supplement. Ivy JL, Goforth HW Jr, Damon BM, McCauley TR, Parsons EC, Price TB. J Appl Physiol. 2002 Oct;93(4):1337-44.

31. Nutrition strategies for the marathon : fuel for training and racing. Burke LM. Sports Med. 2007;37(4-5):344-7.

32. International Society of Sports Nutrition position stand: nutrient timing. Kerksick C, Harvey T, Stout J, Campbell B, Wilborn C, Kreider R, Kalman D, Ziegenfuss T, Lopez H, Landis J, Ivy JL, Antonio J. J Int Soc Sports Nutr. 2008 Oct 3;5:17.

33. What Are Sugar Alcohols? Comparisons and Blood Sugar Impact. Laura Dolson, About.com. April 13, 2009

34. Xylitol chewing gum and dental caries. Tanzer JM. Int Dent J. 1995 Feb;45(1 Suppl 1):65-76. Review.

35. New insights on trehalose: a multifunctional molecule. Elbein AD, Pan YT, Pastuszak I, Carroll D. Glycobiology. 2003 Apr;13(4):17R-27R. Epub 2003 Jan 22.

36. Effects of pre-exercise ingestion of trehalose, galactose and glucose on subsequent metabolism and cycling performance. Jentjens RL, Jeukendrup AE. Eur J Appl Physiol. 2003 Jan;88(4-5):459-65. Epub 2002 Nov 27.

37. Glucose polymer molecular weight does not affect exogenous carbohydrate oxidation. Rowlands DS. et al. Med Sci Sports Exerc. 37: 1510-16. 2005

38. The Influence of starch structure on Glycogen Resynthesis and Subsequent Cycling Performance. Jozsi A.C. et al. Int. J. Sports. Med. 17: 373-378. 1996

39. The Effects of Pre-Exercise Starch Ingestion on Endurance Performance. Goodpaster B.H. et al. Int. J. Sports Med. 17: 366-372. 1996.

40. Improved Gastric Emptying Rate in Humans of a Unique Glucose Polymer with Gel-forming Properties. Leiper J. B. Scan. J. Gastroenterol. 11: 1141-1149. 2000

41. Muscle glycogen resynthesis rate in humans after supplementation of drinks containing carbohydrates with low and high molecular masses. Piehl K. et al. Eur. J. Physiol. 81: 346-351. 2000

42. Setting The Record Straight on the Waxy Maize Craze. Will Brink. 02/24/2009. Muscular Development Magazine Online.

43. The effect of 7 to 8 months of vitamin/mineral supplementation on athletic performance. Telford RD, Catchpole EA, Deakin V, Hahn AG, Plank AW. Int J Sport Nutr. 1992 Jun;2(2):135-53.

44. Riboflavin requirements and exercise adaptation in older women. Winters LR, Yoon JS, Kalkwarf HJ, Davies JC, Berkowitz MG, Haas J, Roe DA. Am J Clin Nutr. 1992 Sep;56(3):526-32.

45. Riboflavin responsive multiple acyl-CoA dehydrogenase deficiency: functional evaluation of recovery after high dose vitamin supplementation. Peluchetti D, Antozzi C, Roi S, DiDonato S, Cornelio F. J Neurol Sci. 1991 Sep;105(1):93-8.

46. Vitamin supplementation and athletic performance. Williams MH. Int J Vitam Nutr Res Suppl. 1989;30:163-91. Review.

47. Effects of pantothenic acid supplementation on human exercise. Littoff D. et al. Med Sci Sports Exerc 1985 17(5-S) 287.

48. Athletic performance and vitamin D. Cannell JJ et al. Med Sci Sports Exerc 2009 Apr 3. [Epub]

49. Alpha-tocopherol supplementation prevents the exercise-induced reduction of serum paraoxonase 1/arylesterase activities in healthy individuals.Tsakiris S, Karikas GA, Parthimos T, Tsakiris T, Bakogiannis C, Schulpis KH. Eur J Clin Nutr. 2009 Feb;63(2):215-21. Epub 2007 Sep 19.

50. Testosterone levels in athletes at rest and exhaustion: effects of calcium supplementation. Cinar V, Baltaci AK, Mogulkoc R, Kilic M. Biol Trace Elem Res. 2009 Summer;129(1-3):65-9. Epub 2008 Dec 20.

51. Sodium phosphate loading improves laboratory cycling time-trial performance in trained cyclists. Folland JP, Stern R, Brickley G. J Sci Med Sport. 2008 Sep;11(5):464-8. Epub 2007 Jun 14.

52. Vitamin and mineral supplementation to athletes. Haymes EM. Int J Sport Nutr. 1991 Jun;1(2):146-69.

53. Acetyl-L-carnitine. Altern Med Rev. Dec;4(6) 438-41. 1999.

54. Carnitine metabolism during exercise. Brass EP, Hiatt WR. Life Sci. 1994;54(19):1383-93.

55. Acetyl-L-carnitine as a precursor of acetylcholine. White HL, Scates PW. Neurochem Res. 1990 Jun;15(6):597-601.

56. Acetyl-L-carnitine treatment stimulates oxygen consumption and biosynthetic function in perfused liver of young and old rats. Mollica MP, Iossa S, Soboll S, Liverini G. Cell Mol Life Sci. 2001 Mar;58(3):477-84.

57. Acetyl-l-carnitine inhibits TNF-alpha-induced insulin resistance via AMPK pathway in rat skeletal muscle cells. Zhang Z, Zhao M, Li Q, Zhao H, Wang J, Li Y. FEBS Lett. 2009 Jan 22;583(2):470-4. Epub 2008 Dec 31.

58. Acetyl-L-carnitine. Altern Med Rev. 1999 Dec;4(6):438-41.

59. A DIGE approach for the assessment of rat soleus muscle changes during unloading: effect of acetyl-L-carnitine supplementation. Moriggi M, Cassano P et al. Proteomics. 2008 Sep;8(17):3588-604.

60. Acetyl-L-carnitine supplementation differently influences nutrient partitioning, serum leptin concentration and skeletal muscle mitochondrial respiration in young and old rats. Iossa S, Mollica MP, Lionetti L, Crescenzo R, Botta M, Barletta A, Liverini G. J Nutr. 2002 Apr;132(4):636-42.

61. Acetyl-L-carnitine administration increases insulin-like growth factor 1 levels in asymptomatic HIV-1-infected subjects: correlation with its suppressive effect on lymphocyte apoptosis and ceramide generation. Di Marzio L, Moretti S, et al. Clin Immunol. 1999 Jul;92(1):103-10.

62. Acetyl L-carnitine (ALC) treatment in elderly patients with fatigue. Malaguarnera M, Gargante MP, Cristaldi E, Colonna V, Messano M, Koverech A, Neri S, Vacante M, Cammalleri L, Motta M. Arch Gerontol Geriatr. 2008 Mar-Apr;46(2):181-90. Epub 2007 Jul 20

63. Exploratory open label, randomized study of acetyl- and propionylcarnitine in chronic fatigue syndrome. Vermeulen RC, Scholte HR. Psychosom Med. 2004 Mar-Apr;66(2):276-82.

64. Anticancer activities of adenine nucleotides in mice are mediated through expansion of erythrocyte ATP pools. Rapaport E, and Fontaine J: Proc. Natl. Acad. Sci. USA 1989; 86:1662-1666

65. ATP executive summary. Eliezer Rapaport, Ph.D. TSI Health Sciences (http://www.peakatp.com/research.php)

66. A randomized, double-blind, placebo controlled triphosphate in study of oral adenosine subacute low back pain.

Bannwarth B, Allaert FA, Avouac B, Rossignol M, Rozenberg S, Valat JP. J Rheumatol. 2005;Jun;32(6):1114-1117

67. Effects of oral ATP supplementation on anaerobic power and muscular strength. Jordan AN, Jurca R. et al. Med Sci Sports Exerc. 2004 Jun;36(6):983-90.

68. Effect of a new cognition enhancer, alpha-glycerylphosphorylcholine, on scopolamine-induced amnesia and brain acetylcholine. Lopez CM, Govoni S. et al. Pharmacol Biochem Behav. 1991 Aug;39(4):835-40.

69. Major mechanisms involved in the synaptic transmission of the neuromuscular apparatus. Rigoard S, Wager M, Buffenoir K, Bauche S, Giot JP, Maixent JM, Rigoard P. Neurochirurgie. 2009 Mar;55 Suppl 1:S22-33. Epub 2009 Feb 20.

70. Contributions of acetylcholine and nitric oxide to forearm blood flow at exercise onset and recovery. Shoemaker JK, Halliwill JR, Hughson RL, Joyner MJ. Am J Physiol. 1997 Nov;273(5 Pt 2):H2388-95.

71. Acute supplementation with alpha-glycerylphosphorylcholine augments growth hormone response to, and peak force production during, resistance exercise. Tim Ziefenfuss et al. JISSN 5:S1 15-16. 2008.

72. Alpha-Glycerophosphocholine in the mental recovery of cerebral ischemic attacks. An Italian multicenter clinical trial. Barbagallo Sangiorgi G, Barbagallo M, Giordano M, Meli M, Panzarasa R. Ann N Y Acad Sci. 1994 Jun 30;717:253-69.

73. Oxidation of leucine and alpha-ketoisocaproate to beta-hydroxy-beta-methylbutyrate in vivo. Van Koevering M, Nissen S. Am J Physiol. 1992 Jan;262(1 Pt 1):E27-31.

74. Nitrogen sparing by 2-ketoisocaproate in parenterally fed rats. Yagi M, Matthews DE, Walser M. Am J Physiol. 1990 Nov;259(5 Pt 1):E633-8.

75. Effects of alpha-ketoisocaproate and of leucine on nitrogen metabolism in postoperative patients. Sapir DG, Stewart PM. Et al. Lancet. 1983 May 7;1(8332):1010-4.

76. alpha-Ketoisocaproate is superior to leucine in sparing glucose utilization in humans. Buckspan R, Hoxworth B, Cersosimo E, Devlin J, Horton E, Abumrad N. Am J Physiol. 1986 Dec;251(6 Pt 1):E648-53.

77. The effects of short-term alpha-ketoisocaproic acid supplementation on exercise performance: a randomized controlled trial. Yarrow JF, Parr JJ, White LJ, Borsa PA, Stevens BR. J Int Soc Sports Nutr. 2007 Jul 13;4:2

78. Influence of alpha-ketoisocaproate on lamb growth, feed conversion, and carcass composition. Flakoll PJ, VandeHaar MJ, Kuhlman G, Nissen S. J Anim Sci. 1991 Apr;69(4):1461-7.

79. The effects of short-term alpha-ketoisocaproic acid supplementation on exercise performance: a randomized controlled trial. Yarrow JF, Parr JJ, White LJ, Borsa PA, Stevens BR. J Int Soc Sports Nutr. 2007 Jul 13;4:2.

80. Alpha-lipoic acid. Jane Higdon, Ph.D. Linus Pauling Institute. Micronutrient Research for Optimum Health. April 10, 2006.

81. Alpha-lipoic acid Monograph. Alternative Medicine Review 11(3) 232-237, 2005

82. Alpha-lipoic acid increases insulin sensitivity by activating AMPK in skeletal muscle. Lee WJ, Song KH, Koh EH, Won JC, Kim HS, Park HS, Kim MS, Kim SW, Lee KU, Park JY. Biochem Biophys Res Commun. 2005 Jul 8;332(3):885-91.

83. Interactions of exercise training and alpha-lipoic acid on insulin signaling in skeletal muscle of obese Zucker rats. Saengsirisuwan V, Perez FR, Sloniger JA, Maier T, Henriksen EJ. Am J Physiol Endocrinol Metab. 2004 Sep;287(3):E529-36. Epub 2004 Apr 6.

84. A-Lipoic acid: effect on glucose uptake, sorbitol pathway, and energy metabolism in experimental diabetic neuropathy. Y Kishi et al. Diabetes 48:2045-51, 1999

85. Studies of energy-linked reactions. Net synthesis of adenosine triphosphate by isolated adenosine triphosphate synthase preparations: a role for lipoic acid and unsaturated fatty acids. Griffiths DE. Biochem J. 1976 Dec 15;160(3):809-12.

86. Interaction of alpha-lipoic acid enantiomers and homologues with the enzyme components of the mamilian pyruvate dehydrogenase complex. Loffelhardt S et al. Biochem Pharmacol 50:637-46, 1995

87. Mitochondrial ageing and the beneficial role of alpha-lipoic acid. Palaniappan AR, Dai A. Neurochem Res. 2007 Sep;32(9):1552-8. Epub 2007 May 3.

88. Enantioselective pharmacokinetics and bioavailability of different racemic alpha-lipoic acid formulations in healthy volunteers. Hermann R, Niebch G, Borbe HO, et al. Eur J Pharm Sci. 1996;4:167-174.

89. Differential effects of lipoic acid stereoisomers on glucose metabolism in insulin-resistant skeletal muscle. Streeper RS, Henriksen EJ, Jacob S, Hokama JY, Fogt DL, Tritschler HJ. Am J Physiol. 1997;273(1 Pt 1):E185-191

90. Improvement of insulin sensitivity in patients with type 2 diabetes mellitus after oral administration of alpha-lipoic acid. Kamenova P. Hormones (Athens). 2006 Oct-Dec;5(4):251-8.

91. Interactions of exercise training and lipoic acid on skeletal muscle glucose transport in obese Zucker rats. Saengsirisuwan V, Kinnick TR, Schmit MB, Henriksen EJ. J Appl Physiol. 2001 Jul;91(1):145-53.

92. Studies on aromatase inhibition with 4-androstene-3,6,17-trione: its 3 beta-reduction and time-dependent irreversible binding to aromatase with human placental microsomes. Numazawa M, Tsuji M, Mutsumi A. J Steroid Biochem 1997, 28:337-44.

93. Aromatase inhibition in the human male reveals a hypothalamic site of estrogen feedback. Hayes F, Seminara S, Decruz S, Boepple P, Crowley W J Clin Endocrinob Metab 2000, 85:3027-35

94. Proof of the effect of testosterone on skeletal muscle. Bhasin S, Woodhouse L, Storer T J Endocrinol 2001, 170:27-38. Bhasin S, Woodhouse L, Storer T

95. Testosterone dose-response relationships in healthy young men. Bhasin S, Woodhouse L, Casaburi R at al. Am J Physiol Endocrinol Metab 2001, 281:E1172-81

96. Low-dose estrogen supplementation improves vascular function in hypogonadal men. Komesaroff PA, Fullerton

M, Esler MD, Dart A, Jennings G, Sudhir K. Hypertension. 2001 Nov;38(5):1011-6.

97. Short-term aromatase inhibition: effects on gucose metabolism and serum leptin levels in young and elderly men. B Lapauw et al. Eur J Endocrinol 160(3): 397-402 (2009).

98. Effects of eight weeks of an alleged aromatase inhibiting nutritional supplement 6-OXO (androst-4-ene-3,6,17-trione) on serum hormone profiles and clinical safety markers in resistance-trained, eugonadal males. Rohle D, Wilborn C, Taylor L, Mulligan C, Kreider R, Willoughby D. J Int Soc Sports Nutr. 2007 Oct 19;4:13.

99. Contribution of meat fat to dietary arachidonic acid. Li D, Ng A, Mann NJ, Sinclair AJ. Lipids. 1998 Apr;33(4):437-40.

100. The Eicosanoids: Prostaglandins, thromboxanes, leukotrienes, & related compounds. E Smith, G FitzGerald. Chapter 18. Basic & Clinical Pharmacology. Bertram Katzung. (LANGE Basic Science). 2007.

101. Prenatal long-chain polyunsaturated fatty acid status: the importance of a balanced intake of docosahexaenoic acid and arachidonic acid. Hadders-Algra M. J Perinat Med. 2008;36(2):101-9.

102. Arachidonic acid metabolism in brain physiology and pathology: lessons from genetically altered mouse models. Bosetti F. J Neurochem. 2007 Aug;102(3):577-86. Epub 2007 Apr 2. Review.

103. Arachidonic-acid-derived eicosanoids: roles in biology and immunopathology. Harizi H, Corcuff JB, Gualde N. Trends Mol Med. 2008 Oct;14(10):461-9. Epub 2008 Sep 4.

104. Arachidonic acid, prostaglandin E2 and F2 alpha influence rates of protein turnover in skeletal and cardiac muscle. Rodemann HP, Goldberg AL. J Biol Chem. 1982 Feb 25;257(4):1632-8.

105. Effect of ibuprofen and acetaminophen on postexercise muscle protein synthesis.Trappe TA, White F, Lambert CP, Cesar D, Hellerstein M, Evans W. Am J Physiol Endocrinol Metab. 2002 Mar;282(3):E551-6.

106. Protein synthesis in isolated forelimb muscles. The possible role of metabolites of arachidonic acid in the response to intermittent stretching. Smith, Palmer et al. Biochem J. 1983 214,153-61

107. Prostaglandin F2 alpha stimulates proliferation of clonal osteoblastic MC3T3-E1 cells by up-regulation of insulin-like growth factor I receptors. Hakeda Y, Harada S, Matsumoto T, Tezuka K, Higashino K, Kodama H, Hashimoto-Goto T, Ogata E, Kumegawa M. J Biol Chem. 1991 Nov 5;266(31):21044-50.

108. Dietary effects of arachidonate-rich fungal oil and fish oil on murine hepatic and hippocampal gene expression. Berger A, Mutch DM, German JB, Roberts MA. Lipids Health Dis. 2002 Oct 21;1:2.

109. The relation between insulin sensitivity and the fatty-acid composition of skeletal-muscle phospholipids. Borkman M, Storlien LH, Pan DA, Jenkins AB, Chisholm DJ, Campbell LV. N Engl J Med. 1993 Jan 28;328(4):238-44.

110. Role of cyclooxygenase-1 and -2 in satellite cell proliferation, differentiation, and fusion. Mendias CL, Tatsumi R, Allen RE. Muscle Nerve. 2004 Oct;30(4):497-500.

111. Prostaglandins are involved in acetylcholine- and 5-hydroxytryptamine-induced, nitric oxide-mediated vasodi-

latation in human forearm. Kamper AM, Paul LC, Blauw GJ. J Cardiovasc Pharmacol. 2002 Dec;40(6):922-9.

112. Relative incorporation of linoleic and arachidonic acid in phospholipids and triglycerides of different rat tissues. Catala A, Brenner RR. Lipids. 1967 Mar;2(2):114-21.

113. Stretch-induced prostaglandins and protein turnover in cultured skeletal muscle. Vandenburgh HH, Hatfaludy S, Sohar I, Shansky J. Am J Physiol. 1990 Aug;259(2 Pt 1):C232-40.

114. Prostaglandins and thromboxanes. Falardeau P, Martineau A, Gagnon D. Sem Hop. 1984 Apr 12;60(16):1117-36.

115. Effects of physical exercise on phospholipid fatty acid composition in skeletal muscle. Andersson A, Sjödin A, Olsson R, Vessby B. Am J Physiol. 1998 Mar;274(3 Pt 1):E432-8.

116. Effects of exercise on parameters of blood coagulation, platelet function and the prostaglandin system. H Sinzinger, I Vergolini. Sports Med 6: 238-45 (1988)

117. Effects of arachidonate-enriched triacylglycerol supplementation on serum fatty acids and platelet aggregation in healthy male subjects with a fish diet. Kusumoto A, Ishikura Y, Kawashima H, Kiso Y, Takai S, Miyazaki M. Br J Nutr. 2007 Sep;98(3):626-35. Epub 2007 Apr 20.

118. Measurement of the incorporation of orally administered arachidonic acid into tissue lipids. R Kulmacz. Lipids 21, 21-25 (1986).

119. Effects of arachidonate-enriched triacylglycerol supplementation on serum fatty acids and platelet aggregation in healthy male subjects with a fish diet. Aki Kusumoto et al. British Journal of Nutrition (2007), 98:626-635.

120. Effects of arachidonic acid supplementation on training adaptations in resistance-trained males. Roberts MD, Iosia M, Kerksick CM, Taylor LW, Campbell B, Wilborn CD, Harvey T, Cooke M, Rasmussen C, Greenwood M, Wilson R, Jitomir J, Willoughby D, Kreider RB. J Int Soc Sports Nutr. 2007 Nov 28;4:21.

121. The Proving Grounds: Arachidonic Acid. W. Llewellyn. Body of Science. Summer 2003. Page 15-19

122. Changes in whole blood and clinical safety markers over 50 days of concomitant arachidonic acid supplementation and resistance training. Wilborn, C, M Roberts, C Kerksick, M Iosia, L Taylor, B Campbell, T Harvey, R Wilson, M. Greenwood, D Willoughby and R Kreider. Proceedings of the International Society of Sports Nutrition (ISSN) Conference June 15-17, 2006.
123. The effect of dietary arachidonic acid on plasma lipoprotein distributions, apoproteins, blood lipid levels, and tissue fatty acid composition in humans. Nelson GJ, Schmidt PC, Bartolini G, Kelley DS, Phinney SD, Kyle D, Silbermann S, Schaefer EJ. Lipids. 1997 Apr;32(4):427-33.

124. Arachidonic acid supplementation enhances synthesis of eicosanoids without suppressing immune functions in young healthy men. Kelley DS, Taylor PC, Nelson GJ, Mackey BE. Lipids. 1998 Feb;33(2):125-30.

125. The effect of dietary arachidonic acid on platelet function, platelet fatty acid composition, and blood coagulation in humans. Nelson GJ, Schmidt PC, Bartolini G, Kelley DS, Kyle D. Lipids. 1997 Apr;32(4):421-5.

126. The relation between insulin sensitivity and the fatty-acid composition of skeletal-muscle phospholipids. Bork-

man M, Storlien LH, Pan DA, Jenkins AB, Chisholm DJ, Campbell LV.N Engl J Med. 1993 Jan 28;328(4):238-44.

127. Omega-6 fatty acids and risk for cardiovascular disease: a science advisory from the American Heart Association Nutrition Subcommittee of the Council on Nutrition, Physical Activity, and Metabolism; Council on Cardiovascular Nursing; and Council on Epidemiology and Prevention. Harris WS, Mozaffarian D, Rimm E, Kris-Etherton P, Rudel LL, Appel LJ, Engler MM, Engler MB, Sacks F. Circulation. 2009 Feb 17;119(6):902-7. Epub 2009 Jan 26.

128. The effect of dietary arachidonic acid on platelet function, platelet fatty acid composition, and blood coagulation in humans. Nelson GJ, Schmidt PC, Bartolini G, Kelley DS, Kyle D. Lipids. 1997 Apr;32(4):421-5.

129. Omega-6 fatty acids and risk for cardiovascular disease: a science advisory from the American Heart Association Nutrition Subcommittee of the Council on Nutrition, Physical Activity, and Metabolism; Council on Cardiovascular Nursing; and Council on Epidemiology and Prevention. Harris WS, Mozaffarian D, Rimm E, Kris-Etherton P, Rudel LL, Appel LJ, Engler MM, Engler MB, Sacks F. Circulation. 2009 Feb 17;119(6):902-7. Epub 2009 Jan 26.

130. Changes in whole blood and clinical safety markers over 50 days of concomitant arachidonic acid supplementation and resistance training. Wilborn, C, M Roberts, C Kerksick, M Iosia, L Taylor, B Campbell, T Harvey, R Wilson, M. Greenwood, D Willoughby and R Kreider. Proceedings of the International Society of Sports Nutrition (ISSN) Conference June 15-17, 2006.

131. Effects of dietary supplementation with arachidonic acid on platelet and renal function in patients with cirrhosis. Pantaleo, P, Marra, F, Vizzutti, F, Spadoni, S, Ciabattoni, G, Galli, C, Villa, GL, Gentilini, P & Laffi, G (2004) Clin Sci 106, 27–34.

132. Relationship of plasma polyunsaturated fatty acids to circulating inflammatory markers. Ferrucci L et al. J Clin Endocrinol Metab 91: 439-46. 2006.

133. Antithetic relationship of dietary arachidonic acid and eicosapentaenoic acid on eicosanoid production in vivo. Li B, Birdwell C, Whelan J. J Lipid Res. 1994 Oct;35(10):1869-77.

134. Arginine: Biochemistry, physiology, and therapeutic implications. A Barbul. JPEN 10(2):227-238 (1986)

135. The ergogenic potential of arginine. B. Campbell, P. La Bounty, M. Roberts. JISSN 1(2):35-38 (2004)

136. Oral arginine attenuates the growth hormone response to resistance exercise. S.R. Collier et al. J Appl Physiol 101: 848-852 (2006)

137. Growth hormone responses to varying doses of oral arginine. Collier SR, Casey DP, Kanaley JA. Growth Horm IGF Res. 2005 Apr;15(2):136-9. Epub 2005 Jan 26.

138. Study on the effect of oral administration of l-arginine on muscular performance in healthy volunteers: an isokinetic study. Santos RS et al. Isokinet Exerc Sci 2002; 10:153-8.

139. Effects of arginine and ornithine on strength, lean body mass and urinary hydroxyproline in adult males. Elam RP, Hardin DH, Sutton RA, Hagen L. J Sports Med Phys Fitness. 1989 Mar;29(1):52-6.

140. Influence of chronic supplementation of arginine aspartate in endurance athletes on performance and substrate

metabolism - a randomized, double-blind, placebo-controlled study. Abel T, Knechtle B, Perret C, Eser P, von Arx P, Knecht H. Int J Sports Med. 2005 Jun;26(5):344-9.

141. No effect of short-term arginine supplementation on nitric oxide production, metabolism and performance in intermittent exercise in athletes. Liu TH, Wu CL, Chiang CW, Lo YW, Tseng HF, Chang CK. J Nutr Biochem. 2009 Jun;20(6):462-8. Epub 2008 Aug 15.

142. Hemodynamic and vascular response to resistance exercise with L-arginine. Fahs CA, Heffernan KS, Fernhall B. Med Sci Sports Exerc. 2009 Apr;41(4):773-9.

143. Potential ergogenic effects of arginine and creatine supplementation. D. Paddon-Jones et al. J. Nutr. 134: 2888S-2894S (2004)

144. The ergogenic potential of arginine. B. Campbell, P. La Bounty, M. Roberts. JISSN 1(2):35-38 (2004)

145. The effect of sodium alpha-ketoglutarate on the physical load endurance of rats with different resistances to hypoxia. Kurhaliuk NM. Fiziol Zh. 2000;46(4):88-95.

146. The use of alpha-ketoglutarate salts in clinical nutrition and metabolic care. Cynober LA. Curr Opin Clin Nutr Metab Care. 1999 Jan;2(1):33-7.

147. Pharmacokinetics, safety, and effects on exercise performance of L-arginine alpha-ketoglutarate in trained adult men. Campbell B, Roberts M, Kerksick C, Wilborn C, Marcello B, Taylor L, Nassar E, Leutholtz B, Bowden R, Rasmussen C, Greenwood M, Kreider R. Nutrition. 2006 Sep;22(9):872-81.

148. Carnosine protects against the inactivation of esterase induced by glycation and a steroid. Yan Hong; Harding John J. Biochimica et biophysica acta 2005;1741(1-2):120-6.

149. Influence of beta-alanine supplementation on skeletal muscle carnosine concentrations and high intensity cycling capacity. C.A. Hill et al. Amino Acids, 2007 Feb;32(2):225-33

150. b-Alanine and the Hormonal Response to Exercise J. Hoffman, N. A. Ratamess et al. Int J Sports Med 2008; 29: 952-958
151. Short-duration beta-alanine supplementation increases training volume and reduces subjective feelings of fatigue in college football players. Hoffman JR, Ratamess NA. et al. Nutr Res. 2008 Jan;28(1):31-5.

152. Effects of beta-alanine supplementation and high-intensity interval training on endurance performance and body composition in men; a double-blind trial. Smith AE, Walter AA et al. J Int Soc Sports Nutr. 2009 Feb 11;6:5.

153. The absorption of orally supplied beta-alanine and its effect on muscle carnosine synthesis in human vastus ateralis. R.C. Harris et al. Amino Acids 30: 279-89 (2006)

154. Betaine in human nutrition. Stuart AS Craig. Am J Clin Nutr 2004; 80:539-49.

155. Influence of betaine consumption on strenuous running and sprinting in a hot environment. Armstrong LE et al. J Strength Cond Res. 2008 May; 22(3):851-60.

156. A further investigation of the role of betaine in transmethylation reactions in vivo. Du Vigneaud V. et al. J Biol Chem 1946, 165:639-48.

157. Effect of betaine supplementation on power performance and fatigue. J Hoffman, N Ratamess et al. J Int Soc Sport Nutr 2009, 6:7

158. The effects of betaine supplementation on strength and power performance. Maresh CM et al. Med Sci Sports Exerc 2008, 39:S101.

159. Influence of betaine consumption on strenuous running and sprinting in a hot environment. Armstrong LE et al. J Strength Cond Res. 2008 May; 22(3):851-60.

160. The total branched-chain amino acid requirement in young healthy adult men determined by indicator amino acid oxidation by use of L-[1-13C]phenylalanine. Riazi R, Wykes LJ, Ball RO, Pencharz PB. J Nutr. 2003 May;133(5):1383-9.

161. Dietary protein impact on glycemic control during weight loss. Layman DK, Baum JI. J Nutr. 2004 Apr;134(4):968S-73S.

162. Nutraceutical effects of branched-chain amino acids on skeletal muscle. Shimomura Y, Yamamoto Y, Bajotto G, Sato J, Murakami T, Shimomura N, Kobayashi H, Mawatari K. J Nutr. 2006 Feb;136(2):529S-532S.

163. Plasma branched-chain amino acid levels and muscle energy metabolism in patients with chronic obstructive pulmonary disease. Kutsuzawa T, Shioya S, Kurita D, Haida M. Clin Nutr. 2009 Apr;28(2):203-8. Epub 2009 Feb 27

164. Branched-chain amino acids and immunity. Calder PC. J Nutr. 2006 Jan;136(1 Suppl):288S-93S. Review.

165. A role for branched-chain amino acids in reducing central fatigue. Blomstrand E. J Nutr. 2006 Feb;136(2):544S-547S.

166. Nutraceutical effects of branched-chain amino acids on skeletal muscle. Shimomura Y, Yamamoto Y, Bajotto G, Sato J, Murakami T, Shimomura N, Kobayashi H, Mawatari K. J Nutr. 2006 Feb;136(2):529S-532S.

167. Exercise promotes BCAA catabolism: effects of BCAA supplementation on skeletal muscle during exercise. Shimomura Y, Murakami T, Nakai N, Nagasaki M, Harris RA. J Nutr. 2004 Jun;134(6 Suppl):1583S-1587S.

168. Leucine-enriched nutrients and the regulation of mammalian target of rapamycin signalling and human skeletal muscle protein synthesis. Drummond MJ, Rasmussen BB. Curr Opin Clin Nutr Metab Care. 2008 May;11(3):222-6.

169. The effects of BCAA and leucine supplementation and lower-body resistance exercise on the ERK 1/2 MAPK pathway signal transduction. Bill Campbell et al. JISSN 2008, 5 (Suppl 1): P19

170. Plasma lactate, GH and GH-binding protein levels in exercise following BCAA supplementation in athletes. De Palo EF, Gatti R, Cappellin E, Schiraldi C, De Palo CB, Spinella P. Amino Acids. 2001;20(1):1-11.

171. Branched-chain amino acids augments ammonia metabolism while attenuating protein breakdown during exercise. MacLean D et al. Am. J. Physiol. 267: E1010-22.

172. Branched-chain amino acids and arginine supplementation attenuates skeletal muscle proteolysis induced by moderate exercise in young individuals. Matsumoto K, Mizuno M, Mizuno T, Dilling-Hansen B, Lahoz A, Bertelsen V, Münster H, Jordening H, Hamada K, Doi T. Int J Sports Med. 2007 Jun;28(6):531-8. Epub 2007 May 11.

173. Exercise promotes BCAA catabolism: effects of BCAA supplementation on skeletal muscle during exercise. Shimomura Y, Murakami T, Nakai N, Nagasaki M, Harris RA. J Nutr. 2004 Jun;134(6 Suppl):1583S-1587S. Review.

174. BCAA intake affects protein metabolism in muscle after but not during exercise in humans. E Blomstrand et al. Am J Physiol Endocrinol Metab 281: E365-74, 2001.

175. Effects of branched-chain amino acid supplementation on serum creatine kinase and lactate dehydrogenase after prolonged exercise. Coombes JS, McNaughton LR. J Sports Med Phys Fitness. 2000 Sep;40(3):240-6.

176. The branched-chain amino acids. Chiarla C, Giovannini I, Boldrini G, Castagneto M. Minerva Gastroenterol Dietol. 1997 Dec;43(4):189-96.

177. Effect of chronic supplementation with branched-chain amino acids on the performance and hepatic and muscle glycogen content in trained rats. de Araujo JA Jr, Falavigna G, Rogero MM, Pires IS, Pedrosa RG, Castro IA, Donato J Jr, Tirapegui J. Life Sci. 2006 Aug 29;79(14):1343-8. Epub 2006 Apr 22.

178. Plasma lactate, GH and GH-binding protein levels in exercise following BCAA supplementation in athletes. De Palo EF, Gatti R, Cappellin E, Schiraldi C, De Palo CB, Spinella P. Amino Acids. 2001;20(1):1-11.

179. Administration of branched-chain amino acids during sustained exercise--effects on performance and on plasma concentration of some amino acids. Blomstrand E, Hassmén P, Ekblom B, Newsholme EA. Eur J Appl Physiol Occup Physiol. 1991;63(2):83-8.

180. Branched-chain amino acids prolong exercise during heat stress in men and women. Mittleman KD, Ricci MR, Bailey SP. Med Sci Sports Exerc. 1998 Jan;30(1):83-91.

181. Effect of acute and chronic branched-chain amino acids on energy metabolism and muscle performance. De Lorenzo A et al. Diabetes Nutr Metab. 2003 Oct-Dec;16(5-6):291-7.

182. Branched-chain amino acid supplementation does not enhance athletic performance but affects muscle recovery and the immune system. Negro M, Giardina S, Marzani B, Marzatico F. J Sports Med Phys Fitness. 2008 Sep;48(3):347-51. Review

183. Branched-chain amino acid supplementation and human performance when hypohydrated in the heat. Cheuvront SN, Carter R 3rd, Kolka MA, Lieberman HR, Kellogg MD, Sawka MN. J Appl Physiol. 2004 Oct;97(4):1275-82.

184. Effects of branched-chain amino acids and carbohydrate on fatigue during intermittent, high-intensity running. Davis JM, Welsh RS, De Volve KL, Alderson NA. Int J Sports Med. 1999 Jul;20(5):309-14.

185. Combined ingestion of protein and free leucine with carbohydrate increases postexercise muscle protein synthesis in vivo in male subjects. Rene´ Koopman et al. Am J Physiol Endocrinol Metab 288: E645–E653, 2005.

186. Determination of the effects of caffeine and carbamazepine on striatal dopamine release by in vivo microdialysis.

Okada M, Kiryu K, Kawata Y, Mizuno K, Wada K, Tasaki H, Kaneko S. Eur J Pharmacol. 1997 Feb 26;321(2):181-8.

187. Studies on the mechanism of caffeine action in alveolar macrophages: caffeine elevates cyclic adenosine monophosphate level and prostaglandin synthesis. M.Jafari, A.Rabbani Metabolism, Volume 53, Issue 6, Pages 687-692

188. Requirement of intact adenosine A1 receptors for the diuretic and natriuretic action of the methylxanthines theophylline and caffeine. Rieg T, Steigele H, Schnermann J, Richter K, Osswald H, Vallon V. J Pharmacol Exp Ther. 2005 Apr;313(1):403-9. Epub 2004 Dec 8.

189. Ergogenic effects of low doses of caffeine on cycling performance. Jenkins NT, Trilk JL, Singhal A, O'Connor PJ, Cureton KJ. Int J Sport Nutr Exerc Metab. 2008 Jun;18(3):328-42.

190. The effect of caffeine ingestion on 8 km run performance in a field setting. Bridge CA, Jones MA. J Sports Sci. 2006 Apr;24(4):433-9.

191. Benefits of caffeine ingestion on sprint performance in trained and untrained swimmers. Collomp K, Ahmaidi S, Chatard JC, Audran M, Préfaut C. Eur J Appl Physiol Occup Physiol. 1992;64(4):377-80.

192. Caffeine and sports performance. L Burke. Appl. Physiol. Nutr. Metab. 33: 1319-34 (2008)

193. Metabolic, catecholamine, and exercise performance responses to various doses of caffeine. Graham T.E. et al. J Appl. Physiol, 78: 867-74 (1995)

194. Carnitine and sports medicine: use or abuse? Brass EP. Ann NY Acad Sci 2004;1033:67-78

195. Carnitine. The science behind a conditionally essential nutrient. Proceedings of a conference. March 25-26, 2004. Bethesda, Maryland, USA. Ann N Y Acad Sci. 2004 Nov;1033:ix-xi; 1-197.

196. Carnitine function and requirements during the life cycle. Rebouche, C.J. et al. 1992. FASEB J. 6: 3379–3386.

197. Exercise physiology in health and disease. Wasserman K, Whipp BJ. Am Rev Resp Dis 112:219–249, 1975.

198. Antioxidant and antiradical activities of L-carnitine. Gülçin I. Life Sci. 2006 Jan 18;78(8):803-11. Epub 2005 Oct 25.

199. Correlation of serum L-carnitine and dehydro-epiandrosterone sulphate levels with age and sex in healthy adults. Chiu KM, Schmidt MJ, Havighurst TC, Shug AL, Daynes RA, Keller ET, Gravenstein S. Age Ageing. 1999 Mar;28(2):211-6.

200. Efficacy of levo carnitine and alpha lipoic acid in ameliorating the decline in mitochondrial enzymes during aging. Savitha S, Sivarajan K, Haripriya D, Kokilavani V, Panneerselvam C. Clin Nutr. 2005 Oct;24(5):794-800.

201. Carnitine. Office of Dietary Supplements. National Institutes of Health. 6/15/2005.

202. Comparison of the Effects of L-Carnitine and Acetyl-L-Carnitine on Carnitine Levels, Ambulatory Activity, and Oxidative Stress Biomarkers in the Brain of Old Rats. Jiankang Liu. Ann. N.Y. Acad. Sci. 1033: 117–131 (2004)

203. The Role of Carnitine and Carnitine Supplementation During Exercise in Man and in Individuals with Special Needs. Eric P. Brass, MD, PhD and William R. Hiatt, MD. Journal of the American College of Nutrition, Vol. 17, No. 3, 207–215 (1998)

204. Studies concerning chronic and acute effects of L-carnitine on some biological parameters in elite athletes. Dragan GI, Vasiliu A, Georgescu E, Dumas I. Physiologie. 1987 Jan-Mar;24(1):23-8.

205. Decrease in respiratory quotient during exercise following L-carnitine supplementation. Gorostiaga EM, Maurer CA, Eclache JP. Int J Sports Med. 1989 Jun;10(3):169-74.

206. Influence of L-carnitine administration on maximal physical exercise. Vecchiet L, Di Lisa F, Pieralisi G, Ripari P, Menabò R, Giamberardino MA, Siliprandi N. Eur J Appl Physiol Occup Physiol. 1990;61(5-6):486-90.

207. Effects of L-carnitine loading on the aerobic and anaerobic performance of endurance athletes. Marconi C, Sassi G, Carpinelli A, Cerretelli P. Eur J Appl Physiol Occup Physiol. 1985;54(2):131-5.

208. Effects of L-carnitine supplementation on physical performance and energy metabolism of endurance-trained athletes: a double-blind crossover field study. Colombani P, Wenk C. et al. Eur J Appl Physiol Occup Physiol. 1996;73(5):434-9.

209. Effect of L-carnitine supplementation on muscle and blood carnitine content and lactate accumulation during high-intensity sprint cycling. Barnett C, Costill DL, Vukovich MD et al. Int J Sport Nutr. 1994 Sep;4(3):280-8.

210. Carnitine supplementation: effect on muscle carnitine and glycogen content during exercise. Vukovich MD, Costill DL, Fink WJ. Med Sci Sports Exerc. 1994 Sep;26(9):1122-9.

211. The effects of L-carnitine supplementation on performance during interval swimming. Trappe SW, Costill DL, Goodpaster B, Vukovich MD, Fink WJ. Int J Sports Med. 1994 May;15(4):181-5.

212. Supplemental carnitine and exercise. E Brass. Am J Clin Nutr 2000; 72(suppl):618S-23S.

213. L-Carnitine supplementation combined with aerobic training does not promote weight loss in moderately obese women. Villani RG, Gannon J, Self M, Rich PA. Int J Sport Nutr Exerc Metab. 2000 Jun;10(2):199-207.

214. Analgesic, anti-inflammatory and venotonic effects of Cissus quadrangularis Linn. Panthong A, Supraditaporn W. et al. J Ethnopharmacol. 2007 Mar 21;110(2):264-70. Epub 2006 Sep 26.

215. Gastroprotective action of Cissus quadrangularis extract against NSAID induced gastric ulcer: role of proinflammatory cytokines and oxidative damage. Jainu M, Devi CS. Chem Biol Interact. 2006 Jul 10;161(3):262-70. Epub 2006 May 1.

216. Antioxidant and antimicrobial activity of Cissus quadrangularis L. Chidambara Murthy KN, Vanitha A, Mahadeva Swamy M, Ravishankar GA. J Med Food. 2003 Summer;6(2):99-105.

217. Gastroprotective effect of Cissus sicyoides (Vitaceae): involvement of microcirculation, endogenous sulfhydryls and nitric oxide. de Paula Ferreira M, Nishijima CM, Seito LN, Dokkedal AL, Lopes-Ferreira M, Di Stasi LC, Vilegas W, Hiruma-Lima CA. J Ethnopharmacol. 2008 Apr 17;117(1):170-4. Epub 2008 Jan 19

218. Studies on cissus quadrangularis linn. I. Acetylcholine like action of the total extract. Das PK, Sanyal AK. Indian J Med Res. 1964 Jan;52:63-7.

219. Inhibitory effects of Cissus quadrangularis L. derived components on lipase, amylase, and alpha-glucosidase activity in-vitro. S. Hollinshead et al. Natl Product Communications 2007, 2:817-22

220. Effect of cissus quadrangularis on the healing of cortisone treated fractures. Prasad GC et al. Indian J Med Res. 1963 Jul;51:667-76

221. The effect of Cissus quadrangularis (CQR-300) and a Cissus formulation (CORE) on obesity and obesity-induced oxidative stress. Oben JE, Enyegue DM, Fomekong GI, Soukontoua YB, Agbor GA. Lipids Health Dis. 2007 Feb 4;6:4.

222. Total-body skeletal muscle mass: evaluation of 24-h urinary creatinine excretion by computerized axial tomography. Wang ZM, Gallagher D, Nelson ME, Matthews DE, Heymsfield SB. Am J Clin Nutr. 1996 Jun;63(6):863-9.

223. The use of a Cissus quadrangularis/Irvingia gabonensis combination in the management of weight loss: a double-blind placebo-controlled study. Oben JE, Ngondi JL, Momo CN, Agbor GA, Sobgui CS. Lipids Health Dis. 2008 Mar 31;7:12.

224. Watermelon consumption increases plasma arginine concentrations in adults. Collins, J. K.; Wu, G.; Perkins-Veazie, P.; Spears, K.; Claypool, P. L.; Baker, R. A.; Clevidence, B. A. Journal: Nutrition. 2007 Mar;23 (3):261-6.

225. Controlled double-blind clinical study against stimol placebo in the treatment of asthenia. Creff AF et al. Gazette Medicale de France. 1982;89:1926-9.

226. Activity of citrulline malate on acid-base balance and blood ammonia and amino acid levels. Study in the animal and in man. Callis A, Magnan de Bornier B, Serrano JJ, Bellet H, Saumade R. Arzneimittelforschung. 1991 Jun;41(6):660-3.

227. Influence of an anti-asthenia agent, citrulline malate, on serum lactate and ammonia kinetics during a maximum exercise test in sedentary subjects. Vanuxem D et al. Seminaire des Hopitaux de Paris. 1990;66:477-81.

228. Citrulline/malate promotes aerobic energy production in human exercising muscle. Bendahan D, Mattei JP, Ghattas B, Confort-Gouny S, Le Guern ME, Cozzone PJ. Br J Sports Med. 2002 Aug;36(4):282-9.

229. Pharmacoclinical approach of citrulline malate activity: analysis of blood lactate during a standardized exercise. Fornaris E et al. Gazette Medicale de France. 1984;91:1-3

230. Influence of an anti-asthenia agent, citrulline malate, on serum lactate and ammonia kinetics during a maximum exercise test in sedentary subjects. Vanuxem D et al. Seminaire des Hopitaux de Paris. 1990;66:477-81.

231. Pharmacological studies on coleonol, a hypotensive diterpene from Coleus forskohlii. Dubey MP, Srimal RC, Nityanand S et al. J Ethnopharmacol. 3:1-13 2006.

232. Forskolin versus sodium cromoglycate for prevention of asthma attacks: a single-blinded clinical trial. González-Sánchez R et al. Int Med Res. 2006 Mar-Apr;34(2):200-7.

233. The effect of forskolin on blood flow, platelet metabolism, aggregation and ATP release. Christenson JT, Thulesius O, Nazzal MM. Vasa. 1995;24(1):56-61.

234. Effects of forskolin on canine congestive heart failure. Sonoki H, Uchida Y, Masuo M, Tomaru T, Katoh A, Sugimoto T. Nippon Yakurigaku Zasshi. 1986 Nov;88(5):389-94.

235. Body composition and hormonal adaptations associated with forskolin consumption in overweight and obese men. Godard MP, Johnson BA, Richmond SR. Obes Res. 2005 Aug;13(8):1335-43.

236. Forskolin lowers intraocular pressure in rabbits, monkeys, and man. Caprioli J, Sears M. Lancet. 1983 Apr 30;1(8331):958-60.

237. Forskolin, adenylate cyclase, and cell physiology: an overview. Daly JW. Adv Cyclic Nucleotide Protein Phosphorylation Res. 1984;17:81-9.

238. Forskolin: a specific stimulator of adenylyl cyclase or a diterpene with multiple sites of action? Laurenza A, Sutkowski EM, Seamon KB. Trends Pharmacol Sci. 1989 Nov;10(11):442-7.

239. Body composition and hormonal adaptations associated with forskolin consumption in overweight and obese men. Godard MP, Johnson BA, Richmond SR. Obes Res. 2005 Aug;13(8):1335-43.

240. Factors affecting conjugated linoleic acid content in milk and meat. Dhiman TR, Nam SH, Ure AL. Crit Rev Food Sci Nutr. 2005;45(6):463-82. Review.

241. A 'good' trans fat? Keith-Thomas Ayoob. ABC News. April 24, 2007.

242. Emerging Health Benefits Of CLA (Conjugated Linoleic Acid). National Dairy Council http://www.national-dairycouncil.org/NationalDairyCouncil/Health/Digest/dcd71-4Page1.htm

243. The potential benefits of creatine and conjugated linoleic acid as adjuncts to resistance training in older adults. M. Tarnopolsky, A. Safdar. Appl. Physiol. Nutr. Metab. 33: 213-27 (2008).

244. Moderate doses of conjugated linoleic acid isomers mix contribute to lowering body fat content maintaining insulin sensitivity and a noninflammatory pattern in adipose tissue in mice. Parra P, Serra F, Palou A. J Nutr Biochem. 2009 Feb 4. [Epub ahead of print]

245. Conjugated linoleic acid prevents growth attenuation induced by corticosteroid administration and increases bone mineral content in young rats.Roy BD, Bourgeois J, Rodriguez C, Payne E, Young K, Shaughnessy SG, Tarnopolosky MA. Appl Physiol Nutr Metab. 2008 Dec;33(6):1096-104.

246. Increased energy metabolism and suppressed body fat accumulation in mice by a low concentration of conjugated linoleic acid. Ohnuki K, Haramizu S, Ishihara K, Fushiki T. Biosci Biotechnol Biochem. 2001 Oct;65(10):2200-4.

247. Effect of conjugated linoleic acid isomers on insulin resistance and mRNA levels of genes regulating energy metabolism in high-fat-fed rats. Choi JS, Jung MH, Park HS, Song J. Nutrition. 2004 Nov-Dec;20(11-12):1008-17.

248. Conjugated linoleic acid supplementation modified the body composition and serum leptin levels in weaning rats. Prais Botelho A, Santos-Zago LF, Costa de Oliveira A. Arch Latinoam Nutr. 2008 Jun;58(2):156-63.

249. Conjugated linoleic acid (CLA) and obesity. Silveira MB, Carraro R, Monereo S, Tébar J. Public Health Nutr. 2007 Oct;10(10A):1181-6. Review.

250. Isomer-specific effects of conjugated linoleic acid on gene expression in RAW 264.7. Lee Y, Thompson JT, de Lera AR, Vanden Heuvel JP. J Nutr Biochem. 2008 Nov 5. [Epub ahead of print]

251. Conjugated linoleic acid isomers: differences in metabolism and biological effects. Churruca I, Fernández-Quintela A, Portillo MP. Biofactors. 2009 Jan-Feb;35(1):105-11. Review.

252. Differential effects of conjugated linoleic acid isomers in insulin-resistant female C57Bl/6J mice. Halade GV, Rahman MM, Fernandes G. J Nutr Biochem. 2009 May 6. [Epub ahead of print]

253. The effects of conjugated linoleic acid supplementation during resistance training. Pinkoski C, Chilibeck PD, Candow DG, Esliger D, Ewaschuk JB, Facci M, Farthing JP, Zello GA. Med Sci Sports Exerc. 2006 Feb;38(2):339-48.

254. Effects of conjugated linoleic acid supplementation during resistance training on body composition, bone density, strength, and selected hematological markers. Kreider RB, Ferreira MP, Greenwood M, Wilson M, Almada AL. J Strength Cond Res. 2002 Aug;16(3):325-34.

255. Conjugated linoleic acid supplementation for twelve weeks increases lean body mass in obese humans. Steck SE, Chalecki AM, Miller P. J Nutr. 2007 May;137(5):1188-93.

256. Creatine: biosynthesis, regulation, and function. Walker J. Adv Enzym 50:117-242 (1979)

257. Creatine supplementation enhances anaerobic ATP synthesis during a single 10 sec maximal handgrip exercise. Kurosawa Y, Hamaoka T, Katsumura T, Kuwamori M, Kimura N, Sako T, Chance B. Mol Cell Biochem. 2003 Feb;244(1-2):105-12.

258. Creatine: biosynthesis, regulation, and function. Walker J. Adv Enzym 50:117-242 (1979)

259. Potential ergogenic effects of arginine and creatine supplementation. D Paddon-Jones et al. J Nutr 134:2888S-2894S, 2004.

260. Creatine supplementation during resistance training in college football athletes. Bemben MG, Bemben DA, Loftiss DD, Knehans AW. Med Sci Sports Exerc. 2001 Oct;33(10):1667-73.

261. Effects of acute creatine monohydrate supplementation on leucine kinetics and mixed-muscle protein synthesis. Parise G, Mihic S, MacLennan D, Yarasheski KE, Tarnopolsky MA. J Appl Physiol. 2001 Sep;91(3):1041-7.

262. Effect of creatine supplementation and resistance-exercise training on muscle insulin-like growth factor in young adults. Burke DG, Candow DG, Chilibeck PD, MacNeil LG, Roy BD, Tarnopolsky MA, Ziegenfuss T. Int J Sport Nutr Exerc Metab. 2008 Aug;18(4):389-98.

263. Increased IGF mRNA in human skeletal muscle after creatine supplementation. Deldicque L, Louis M, Theisen D, Nielens H, Dehoux M, Thissen JP, Rennie MJ, Francaux M. Med Sci Sports Exerc. 2005 May;37(5):731-6.

264. Effects of oral creatine and resistance training on myogenic regulatory factor expression.Willoughby DS, Rosene JM. Med Sci Sports Exerc. 2003 Jun;35(6):923-9.

265. Dietary creatine monohydrate supplementation increases satellite cell mitotic activity during compensatory hypertrophy. Dangott B, Schultz E, Mozdziak PE. Int J Sports Med. 2000 Jan;21(1):13-6.

266. Clinical pharmacology of the dietary supplement creatine monohydrate. Persky AM, Brazeau GA. Pharmacol Rev. 2001 Jun;53(2):161-76.

267. Creatine in sports. Kreider RB. Essentials of Sport Nutrition & Supplements. Humana Oress. Totowa, NJ. 2007.

268. Creatine supplementation: a comparison of loading and maintenance protocols on creatine uptake by human skeletal muscle. Preen D, Dawson B, Goodman C, Beilby J, Ching S. Int J Sport Nutr Exerc Metab. 2003 Mar;13(1):97-111.

269. Muscle creatine loading in men. Hultman E. et al. J Appl Physiol 81:232-37. (1996)

270. Kinetics of creatine ingestion as a food ingredient. Deldicque L et al. Eur J Appl Physiol 2008, 102(2): 133-43.

271. International Society of Sports Nutrition position stand: creatine supplementation and exercise. Buford TW, Kreider RB, Stout JR, Greenwood M, Campbell B, Spano M, Ziegenfuss T, Lopez H, Landis J, Antonio J. J Int Soc Sports Nutr. 2007 Aug 30;4:6.

272. Performance and muscle fiber adaptations to creatine supplementation and heavy resistance training. Volek JS, Duncan ND, Mazzetti SA, Staron RS, Putukian M, Gómez AL, Pearson DR, Fink WJ, Kraemer WJ. Med Sci Sports Exerc. 1999 Aug;31(8):1147-56.

273. Effect of in-season creatine supplementation on body composition and performance in rugby union football players. Chilibeck PD, Magnus C, Anderson M. Appl Physiol Nutr Metab. 2007 Dec;32(6):1052-7.

274. The effects of acute creatine supplementation on multiple sprint cycling and running performance in rugby players. Ahmun RP, Tong RJ, Grimshaw PN. J Strength Cond Res. 2005 Feb;19(1):92-7.

275. Effects of creatine monohydrate supplementation on body composition and strength indices in experienced resistance trained women. Ferguson TB, Syrotuik DG. J Strength Cond Res. 2006 Nov;20(4):939-46.

276. Creatine fails to augment the benefits from resistance training in patients with HIV infection: a randomized, double-blind, placebo-controlled study. Sakkas GK, Mulligan K, Dasilva M, Doyle JW, Khatami H, Schleich T, Kent-Braun JA, Schambelan M.
PLoS One. 2009;4(2):e4605. Epub 2009 Feb 26.

277. Effect of creatine supplementation on body composition and performance: a meta-analysis.Branch JD. Int J Sport Nutr Exerc Metab. 2003 Jun;13(2):198-226.

278. The effects of creatine ethyl ester supplementation combined with heavy resistance training on body composition, muscle performance, and serum and muscle creatine levels. Spillane M, Schoch R, Cooke M, Harvey T, Greenwood M, Kreider R, Willoughby DS. J Int Soc Sports Nutr. 2009 Feb 19;6:6.

279. Non-Enzymatic Hydrolysis of Creatine Ethyl Ester. Katseres NS, Reading DW, Shayya L, Dicesare JC, Purser GH. Biochem Biophys Res Commun. 2009 Jun 11. [Epub ahead of print]

280. The effects of creatine pyruvate and creatine citrate on performance during high intensity exercise. Jäger R, Metzger J, Lautmann K, Shushakov V, Purpura M, Geiss KR, Maassen N. J Int Soc Sports Nutr. 2008 Feb 13;5:4.

281. Comparison of new forms of creatine in raising plasma creatine levels. Jäger R, Harris RC, Purpura M, Francaux M. J Int Soc Sports Nutr. 2007 Nov 12;4:17.

282. The effects of creatine pyruvate and creatine citrate on performance during high intensity exercise. Jäger R, Metzger J, Lautmann K, Shushakov V, Purpura M, Geiss KR, Maassen N. J Int Soc Sports Nutr. 2008 Feb 13;5:4.

283. Edustusmelojat testasivat kreatiinipyruvaatin. Nuuttilla S. Suomen Urheilulehti 2000, 23(S); 4.

284. Comparison of new forms of creatine in raising plasma creatine levels. Jäger R, Harris RC, Purpura M, Francaux M. J Int Soc Sports Nutr. 2007 Nov 12;4:17.

285. Magnesium-creatine supplementation effects on body water. Brilla LR, Giroux MS, Taylor A, Knutzen KM. Metabolism. 2003 Sep;52(9):1136-40.

286. Mg2+-creatine chelate and a low-dose creatine supplementation regimen improve exercise performance. Selsby JT, DiSilvestro RA, Devor ST. J Strength Cond Res. 2004 May;18(2):311-5.

287. Effect of oral creatine supplementation on skeletal muscle phosphocreatine resynthesis. Greenhaff PL, Bodin K, Soderlund K, Hultman E. Am J Physiol. 1994 May;266(5 Pt 1):E725-30.

288. Creatine supplementation: a comparison of loading and maintenance protocols on creatine uptake by human skeletal muscle. Preen, D. et al. Int J Sport Nutr Exerc Metab. 13: 97-111 (2003).

289. Creatine supplementation: a comparison of loading and maintenance protocols on creatine uptake by human skeletal muscle. Preen D, Dawson B, Goodman C, Beilby J, Ching S. Int J Sport Nutr Exerc Metab. 2003 Mar;13(1):97-111.

290. Long-term creatine supplementation is safe in aged patients with Parkinson disease. Bender A, Samtleben W, Elstner M, Klopstock T. Nutr Res. 2008 Mar;28(3):172-8.

291. DHEA and its transformation into androgens and estrogens in peripheral target tissues: intracrinology. Labrie F, Luu-The V, Labrie C, Simard J. Front Neuroendocrinol. 2001 Jul;22(3):185-212.

292. Dehydroepiandrosterone and its metabolites: Differential effects on androgen receptor trafficking and transcriptional activity. Qianxing Mo, Shi-fang Lu and Neal G. Simon. The Journal of Steroid Biochemistry and Molecular Biology. Volume 99, Issue 1, April 2006, Pages 50-58

293. Impact of DHEA(S) and cortisol on immune function in aging: a brief review. Buford TW, Willoughby DS. Appl Physiol Nutr Metab. 2008 Jun;33(3):429-33.

294. Actions of dehydroepiandrosterone and its sulfate in the central nervous system: effects on cognition and emotion in animals and humans. Wolf OT, Kirschbaum C. Brain Res Brain Res Rev. 1999 Nov;30(3):264-88. Review.

295. Effect of DHEA on Abdominal Fat and Insulin Action in Elderly Women and Men A Randomized Controlled Trial Dennis T. Villareal, MD; John O. Holloszy, MD. JAMA. 2004;292:2243-2248.

296. Anti-glucocorticoid effects of dehydroepiandrosterone (DHEA). Kalimi M et al. Mol Cell Biochem 131: 99-104, 1994

297. Effects of aging on dehydroepiandrosterone sulfate in relation to fasting insulin levels and body composition assessed by bioimpedance analysis. Denti L, Pasolini G, Sanfelici L, et al. Metabolism 1997, 46(7):826-32.

298. Changes in serum concentrations of conjugated and unconjugated steroids in 40- to 80- year old men. Belanger A et al. J Clin Endocrinol Metab 79: 1086-90, 1994

299. Replacement and supplementation of DHEA--is it a wellness hormone? Brückel J. MMW Fortschr Med. 2005 Feb 17;147(7):30-2. Review

300. DHEA therapy for women: effect on sexual function and wellbeing. Panjari M, Davis SR. Hum Reprod Update. 2007 May-Jun;13(3):239-48. Epub 2007 Jan 5.

301. Dehydroepiandrosterone reduces serum low density lipoprotein levels and body fat but does not alter insulin sensitivity in normal men. Nestler JE, Barlascini CO, Clore JN, Blackard WG. J Clin Endocrinol Metab. 1988 Jan;66(1):57-61.

302. Supplementation with DHEA: effect on muscle size, strength, quality of life, and lipids Dayal M, Sammel MD, Zhao J, Hummel AC, Vandenbourne K, Barnhart KT. J Womens Health (Larchmt). 2005 Jun;14(5):391-400.

303. Effects of replacement dose of dehydroepiandrosterone in men and women of advancing age. Morales AJ, Nolan JJ, Nelson JC, Yen SS. J Clin Endocrinol Metab. 1994 Jun;78(6):1360-7.

304. DHEA enhances effects of weight training on muscle mass and strength in elderly women and men. Villareal DT, Holloszy JO. Am J Physiol Endocrinol Metab. 2006 Nov;291(5):E1003-8. Epub 2006 Jun 20.

305. Dehydroepiandrosterone reduces serum low density lipoprotein levels and body fat but does not alter insulin sensitivity in normal men. Nestler JE, Barlascini CO, Clore JN, Blackard WG. J Clin Endocrinol Metab. 1988 Jan;66(1):57-61.

306. DHEA enhances effects of weight training on muscle mass and strength in elderly women and men. Dennis T. Villareal and John O. Holloszy. Am J Physiol Endocrinol Metab 291:1003-1008, 2006.

307. Effect of oral DHEA on serum testosterone and adaptations to resistance training in young men. Brown GA, Vukovich MD, Sharp RL, Reifenrath TA, Parsons KA, King DS. J Appl Physiol. 1999 Dec;87(6):2274-83.

308. Effects of dehydroepiandrosterone vs androstenedione supplementation in men. Wallace MB, Lim J, Cutler A, Bucci L. Med Sci Sports Exerc. 1999 Dec;31(12):1788-92.

309. Practical uses for ecdysteroids in mammals including humans: and update. Lafont R., Dinan L. Journal of Insect Science. 3:7 (2003)

310. The effect of Elton, leveton, fitoton and adapton on the work capacity of experimental animals. Azizov AP, Seifulla RD. 1998. Eksperimental'naya I Klinicheskaya Farmakologiya 61:61-63.

311. Effect of vitamin D3 and 20-hydroxyecdysone on the content of ATP, creatine phosphate, carnosine and Ca2+ in skeletal muscles. Kholodova IuD, Tuga? VA, Zimina VP. Ukr Biokhim Zh. 1997 May-Jun;69(3):3-9.

312. Effect of 20-hydroxyecdysone on the protein synthesis of pigs. Opletal, F. et al. Zivocisna Vyroba 42: 445-51 (1997).

313. Stimulation of growth and development in Japanese quails after oral administration of ecdysteroid-containing diet. Koudela, K. et al. Eur J Entomology 92: 349-354 (1995)

314. The combined use of Ecdisten and the product 'Bodrost' during training in cyclical types of sport. Simakin, S.Y. et al. Scientific Sports Bulletin, 1988. 2.

315. A comparative study of the anabolic action of ecdysten, leveton and Prime Plus, preparations of plant origin. Gadzhieva RM, Portugalov SN, Paniushkin VV, Kondrat'eva II. Eksp Klin Farmakol. 1995 Sep-Oct;58(5):46-8.

316. The action of methandrostenolone and ecdysterone on the physical endurance of animals and on protein metabolism in the skeletal muscles. Chermnykh NS, Shimanovski? NL, Shutko GV, Syrov VN. Farmakol Toksikol. 1988 Nov-Dec;51(6):57-60.

317. Effects of methoxyisoflavone, ecdysterone, and sulfo-polysaccharide supplementation on training adaptations in resistance-trained males. Wilborn CD, Taylor LW, Campbell BI, Kerksick C, Rasmussen CJ, Greenwood M, Kreider RB. J Int Soc Sports Nutr. 2006 Dec 13;3:19-27.

318. Insect hormones – ecdysteroids: their presence and actions in vertebrates. Slama K, Lafont R. Eur J Entomology 92: 355-77 (1995).

319. Therapeutic applications of fenugreek. Basch E, Ulbricht C, Kuo G. Altern Med Rev. 2003 Feb;8(1):20-7.

320. Fattening practices among Moroccan Saharawi women. Rguibi M, Belahsen R. East Mediterr Health J. 2006 Sep;12(5):619-24.

321. Hydroxyisoleucine: a novel amino acid potentiator of insulin action. Sauvaire Y et al. Diabetes 47:206-10. (1998)

322. Effect of fenugreek seeds on intravenous glucose disposition in non-insulin dependant diabetic patients. Raghuram TC et al. Phytother Res 8:83-6 (1994)

323. Effect of Trigonela foenum graceum on blood glucose levels in normal and alloxan-diabetic mice. Ajabnoor MA et al. Ethnopharmacol 22:45-49 (1988)

324. Therapeutic applications of Fenugreek. Basch E et al. Alt Med Rev 8(1): 20-27 (2003)

325. The effect of an ethanol extract derived from fenugreek (Trigonela foenum graceum) on bile acid absorption and cholesterol levels in rats. Stark A. et al. Br J Nutr 69:277-87 (1993)

326. Diosgenin--a growth stimulator of mammary gland of ovariectomized mouse. Aradhana. Rao AR. Kale RK. (1992) Indian Journal of Experimental Biology, 30(5):367-70

327. Rat growth-hormone release stimulators from fenugreek seeds. Shim SH, Lee EJ, Kim JS, Kang SS, Ha H, Lee HY, Kim C, Lee JH, Son KH. Chem Biodivers. 2008 Sep;5(9):1753-61.

328. The addition of fenugreek extract (Trigonella foenum-graecum) to glucose feeding increases muscle glycogen resynthesis after exercise. Ruby BC, Gaskill SE, Slivka D, Harger SG. Amino Acids. 2005 Feb;28(1):71-6. Epub 2004 Dec 2

329. Effects of fenugreek seeds (Trigonella foenum greaecum) extract on endurance capacity in mice. Ikeuchi M, Yamaguchi K, Koyama T, Sono Y, Yazawa K. J Nutr Sci Vitaminol (Tokyo). 2006 Aug;52(4):287-92.

330. Omega-3 fatty acids, exercise, physical activity and athletics. Simopoulos AP. World Rev Nutr Diet. 2008;98:23-50. Review.

331. Omega-3 polyunsaturated fatty acids and human health outcomes. Calder PC, Yaqoob P. Biofactors. 2009 May-Jun;35(3):266-72.

332. Roles of unsaturated fatty acids (especially omega-3 fatty acids) in the brain at various ages and during ageing. Bourre JM. J Nutr Health Aging. 2004;8(3):163-74. Review.

333. Fish oil and the management of hypertriglyceridemia.Mattar M, Obeid O. Nutr Health. 2009;20(1):41-9. Review.

334. The effect of omega-3 fatty acids on risk factors for cardiovascular diseases. Yam D, Bott-Kanner G, Genin I, Shinitzky M, Klainman E. Harefuah. 2001 Dec;140(12):1156-8, 1230.

335. Fish oil fatty acids improve postprandial vascular reactivity in healthy men. Armah CK, Jackson KG, Doman I, James L, Cheghani F, Minihane AM. Clin Sci (Lond). 2008 Jun;114(11):679-86

336. Fish oil supplementation improves endothelial function in normoglycemic offspring of patients with type 2 diabetes. Rizza S, Tesauro M, Cardillo C, Galli A, Iantorno M, Gigli F, Sbraccia P, Federici M, Quon MJ, Lauro D. Atherosclerosis. 2009 Mar 19

337. Fish consumption, omega 3 fatty acids and cardiovascular disease. The science and the clinical trials. Galli C, Risé P. Nutr Health. 2009;20(1):11-20. Review.

338. Omega-3 fatty acids from fish oils and cardiovascular disease. Holub DJ, Holub BJ. Mol Cell Biochem. 2004 Aug;263(1-2):217-25.

339. Evidence for the cardioprotective effects of omega-3 Fatty acids. Carroll DN, Roth MT. Ann Pharmacother. 2002 Dec;36(12):1950-6.

340. Omega-3 fatty acids and inflammation. Mori TA, Beilin LJ. Curr Atheroscler Rep. 2004 Nov;6(6):461-7. Review

341. Therapeutic potential of n-3 polyunsaturated fatty acids in disease. Fetterman JW Jr, Zdanowicz MM. Am J Health Syst Pharm. 2009 Jul 1;66(13):1169-79.

342. Fish oil and inflammatory disease: is asthma the next target for n-3 fatty acid supplements?. Stephensen, C.B. 2004. Nutrition Reviews. 62(12):486-9.

343. Cognitive and physiological effects of Omega-3 polyunsaturated fatty acid supplementation in healthy subjects. Fontani G, Corradeschi F, Felici A, Alfatti F, Migliorini S, Lodi L. Eur J Clin Invest. 2005 Nov;35(11):691-9.

344. The pathophysiology and treatment of cancer cachexia. Barber MD. Nutr Clin Pract. 2002 Aug;17(4):203-9.

345. Cancer cachexia and its treatment with fish-oil-enriched nutritional supplementation. Barber MD. Nutrition. 2001 Sep;17(9):751-5. Review.

346. Omega-3 fatty acids, exercise, physical activity and athletics. Simopoulos AP. World Rev Nutr Diet. 2008;98:23-50. Review.

347. Anti-obesity effects of long-chain omega-3 polyunsaturated fatty acids. Buckley JD, Howe PR. Obes Rev. 2009 May 12. [Epub ahead of print]

348. Dietary fish oil alters cardiomyocyte Ca2+ dynamics and antioxidant status. Jahangiri A, Leifert WR, Kind KL, McMurchie EJ. Free Radic Biol Med. 2006 May 1;40(9):1592-602. Epub 2006 Jan 18.

349. Supplementation with omega-3 polyunsaturated fatty acids augments brachial artery dilation and blood flow during forearm contraction. Walser B, Giordano RM, Stebbins CL. Eur J Appl Physiol. 2006 Jun;97(3):347-54. Epub 2006 Apr 25.

350. The effects of ingestion of omega-3 fatty acids on perceived pain and external symptoms of delayed onset muscle soreness in untrained men. Tartibian B, Maleki BH, Abbasi A. Clin J Sport Med. 2009 Mar;19(2):115-9.

351. Fish oil supplementation reduces severity of exercise-induced bronchoconstriction in elite athletes. Mickleborough TD, Murray RL, Ionescu AA, Lindley MR. Am J Respir Crit Care Med. 2003 Nov 15;168(10):1181-9. Epub 2003 Aug 6.

352. Omega-3 fatty acids, exercise, physical activity and athletics. Simopoulos AP. World Rev Nutr Diet. 2008;98:23-50. Review.

353. DHA-rich fish oil lowers heart rate during submaximal exercise in elite Australian Rules footballers. Buckley JD, Burgess S, Murphy KJ, Howe PR. J Sci Med Sport. 2009 Jul;12(4):503-507. Epub 2008 Jun 13.

354. Fish oil reduces heart rate and oxygen consumption during exercise. Peoples GE, McLennan PL, Howe PR, Groeller H. J Cardiovasc Pharmacol. 2008 Dec;52(6):540-7.

355. Effect of n-3 fatty acids on free Tryptophan and exercise fatigue. Huffman DM et al. Eur J Appl Physiol 2004 Aug; 92(4-5): 584-91 Epub.

William Llewellyn's SPORT SUPPLEMENT REFERENCE GUIDE

356. The role of fish oil in hypertension. Yang H, Kenny A. Conn Med. 2007 Oct;71(9):533-8.

357. Gamma-oryzanol: an important component in rice brain oil. Scavariello EM, Arellano DB. Arch Latinoam Nutr. 1998 Mar;48(1):7-12

358. Effects of gamma-oryzanol on serum lipids and apolipoproteins in dyslipidemic schizophrenics receiving major tranquilizers. Sasaki J, Takada Y, Handa K, Kusuda M, Tanabe Y, Matsunaga A, Arakawa K. Clin Ther. 1990 May-Jun;12(3):263-8.

359. Effects of gamma-oryzanol on gastric lesions and small intestinal propulsive activity in mice. Ichimaru Y, Moriyama M, Ichimaru M, Gomita Y. Nippon Yakurigaku Zasshi. Dec1984;84(6):537-42

360. Clinical studies of oral administration of gamma-oryzanol on climacteric complaints and its syndrome. Murase Y, Iishima H. Obstet Gynecol Prac. 1963;12:147-9

361. Gamma oryzanol-plant sterol supplementation: metabolic, endocrine, and physiologic effects. Wheeler KB, Garleb KA. Int J Sport Nutr. Jun1991;1(2):170-7.

362. The effect of gamma-oryzanol on rat pituitary hormone secretion (author's transl). Yamauchi J, Takahara J, Uneki T, Yakushiji W, Nakashima Y, Miyoshi M, Ofuji T. Nippon Naibunpi Gakkai Zasshi. 1980 Aug 20;56(8):1130-9.

363. Pituitary and thyroid hormone responses of heifers after ferulic acid administration. Gorewit RC. J Dairy Sci. 1983 Mar;66(3):624-9.

364. The effects of gamma-oryzanol supplementation during resistance exercise training. Fry AC, Bonner E, Lewis DL, et al. Int J Sport Nutr. Dec1997;7(4):318-29.

365. Glutamine and glutamate as vital metabolites. P. Newsholme et al. Braz J Med Biol Res 36(2): 153-163, 2003.

366. Is glutamine a conditionally essential amino acid? Lacey JM, Wilmore DW. Nutr Rev. 1990 Aug;48(8):297-309. Review.

367. Glutamine and glutamate as vital metabolites. P. Newsholme et al. Braz J Med Biol Res 36(2): 153-163, 2003.

368. Glutamine transport and its metabolic effects. Rennie MJ, Tadros L, Khogali S, Ahmed A, Taylor PM. J Nutr. 1994 Aug;124(8 Suppl):1503S-1508S.

369. Glutamine metabolism and transport in skeletal muscle and heart and their clinical relevance. Rennie MJ, Ahmed A, Khogali SE, Low SY, Hundal HS, Taylor PM. J Nutr. 1996 Apr;126(4 Suppl):1142S-9S. Review.

370. Glutamine: effects on the immune system, protein balance and intestinal functions] Roth E, Spittler A, Oehler R. Wien Klin Wochenschr. 1996;108(21):669-76. Review.

371. L-glutamine supplementation induces insulin resistance in adipose tissue and improves insulin signalling in liver and muscle of rats with diet-induced obesity. Prada PO, Hirabara SM, de Souza CT, Schenka AA, Zecchin HG, Vassallo J, Velloso LA, Carneiro E, Carvalheira JB, Curi R, Saad MJ. Diabetologia. 2007 Sep;50(9):1949-59. Epub 2007 Jun 29.

372. The effect of glutamine on prevention of glucocorticoid-induced skeletal muscle atrophy is associated with myo-statin suppression. Salehian B, Mahabadi V, Bilas J, Taylor WE, Ma K. Metabolism. 2006 Sep;55(9):1239-47.

373. Interaction between glutamine availability and metabolism of glycogen, tricarboxylic acid cycle intermediates and glutathione. Rennie MJ, Bowtell JL, Bruce M, Khogali SE. J Nutr. 2001 Sep;131(9 Suppl):2488S-90S; discussion 2496S-7S.

374. Effect of oral glutamine on whole body carbohydrate storage during recovery from exhaustive exercise. Bowtell JL, Gelly K, Jackman ML, Patel A, Simeoni M, Rennie MJ. J Appl Physiol. 1999 Jun;86(6):1770-7.

375. Glutamine supplementation further enhances exercise-induced plasma IL-6. Hiscock N, Petersen EW, Krzywkowski K, Boza J, Halkjaer-Kristensen J, Pedersen BK. J Appl Physiol. 2003 Jul;95(1):145-8. Epub 2003 Feb 28.

376. The biological roles of exercise-induced cytokines: IL-6, IL-8, and IL-15. Nielsen AR, Pedersen BK. Appl Physiol Nutr Metab. 2007 Oct;32(5):833-9.

377. Glutamine and carbohydrate supplements reduce ammonemia increase during endurance field exercise. Carvalho-Peixoto J, Alves RC, Cameron LC. Appl Physiol Nutr Metab. 2007 Dec;32(6):1186-90.

378. Effects of supply with glutamine on antioxidant system and lipid peroxidation in patients with parenteral nutrition. Abilés J, Moreno-Torres R, Moratalla G, Castaño J, Pérez Abúd R, Mudarra A, Machado MJ, Planells E, Pérez de la Cruz A. Nutr Hosp. 2008 Jul-Aug;23(4):332-9.

379. The effects of oral glutamine supplementation on athletes after prolonged, exhaustive exercise. Castell LM, Newsholme EA. Nutrition. 1997 Jul-Aug;13(7-8):738-42.

380. Glutamine and the effects of exhaustive exercise upon the immune response. Castell LM, Newsholme EA. Can J Physiol Pharmacol. 1998 May;76(5):524-32. Review.

381. Enteral glutamine increases growth and absorptive capacity of intestinal mucosa in the malnourished rat. Wirén M, Magnusson KE, Larsson J. Scand J Gastroenterol. 1995 Feb;30(2):146-52.

382. Glutamine supplementation. Heal the gut, help the patient. Savy GK. J Infus Nurs. 2002 Jan-Feb;25(1):65-9. Review.

383. Effect of oral glutamine on whole body carbohydrate storage during recovery from exhaustive exercise. Bowtell JL, Gelly K, Jackman ML, Patel A, Simeoni M, Rennie MJ. J Appl Physiol. 1999 Jun;86(6):1770-7.

384. Effect of exercise on protein turnover in man. Rennie MJ, Edwards RH, Krywawych S, Davies CT, Halliday D, Waterlow JC, Millward DJ. Clin Sci (Lond). 1981 Nov;61(5):627-39.

385. Whole body and skeletal muscle glutamine metabolism in healthy subjects. Mittendorfer B, Volpi E, Wolfe RR. Am J Physiol Endocrinol Metab. 2001 Feb;280(2):E323-33.

386. Plasma glutamine response to enteral administration of glutamine in human volunteers (free glutamine versus protein-bound glutamine). Boza JJ, Maire J, Bovetto L, Ballèvre O. Nutrition. 2000 Nov-Dec;16(11-12):1037-42.

387. Peptide glutamine supplementation for tolerance of intermittent exercise in soccer players. Favano A, Santos-Silva PR, Nakano EY, Pedrinelli A, Hernandez AJ, Greve JM. Clinics (Sao Paulo). 2008 Feb;63(1):27-32.

388. Addition of glutamine to essential amino acids and carbohydrate does not enhance anabolism in young human males following exercise. Wilkinson SB, Kim PL, Armstrong D, Phillips SM. Appl Physiol Nutr Metab. 2006 Oct;31(5):518-29.

389. Acute L-glutamine ingestion does not improve maximal effort exercise. Haub MD, Potteiger JA, Nau KL, Webster MJ, Zebas CJ. J Sports Med Phys Fitness. 1998 Sep;38(3):240-4.

390. No effect of glutamine supplementation and hyperoxia on oxidative metabolism and performance during high-intensity exercise. Marwood S, Bowtell J. J Sports Sci. 2008 Aug;26(10):1081-90.

391. The effects of high-dose glutamine ingestion on weightlifting performance. Antonio J, Sanders MS, Kalman D, Woodgate D, Street C. J Strength Cond Res. 2002 Feb;16(1):157-60.

392. Acute L-glutamine ingestion does not improve maximal effort exercise. Haub MD, Potteiger JA, Nau KL, Webster MJ, Zebas CJ. J Sports Med Phys Fitness. 1998 Sep;38(3):240-4.

393. Dosing and efficacy of glutamine supplementation in human exercise and sport training. Gieeson M. J Nutr. 2008 Oct;138(10: 2045S-2049S.

394. Exploring the potential ergogenic effects of glycerol hyperhydration. Nelson JL, Roberts RA. Sports Med. 2007;37(11) 981-1000.

395. Hyperhydrating with glycerol: implications for athletic performance. Wagner DR. J Am Diet Assoc. 1999 Feb;99(2);207-12.

396. Comparison of glycerol and water hydration regimens on tennis-related performance. Magal M, Webster MJ, Sistrunk LE, Whitehead MT, Evans RK, Boyd JC. Med Sci Sports Exerc. 2003 Jan;35(1):150-6.

397. Oral glycerine has a negligible effect on plasma glucose and insulin in normal subjects. Diabetes 2002;51(Supplement 2):A602.

398. Comparison of the effects of pre-exercise feeding of glucose, glycerol and placebo on endurance and fuel homeostasis in man. Gleeson M, Maughan RJ, Greenhaff PL. Eur J Appl Physiol Occup Physiol. 1986;55(6):645-53.

399. The effect of glycerol hyperhydration on olympic distance triathlon performance in high ambient temperatures. Coutts A, Reaburn P, Mummery K, Holmes M. Int J Sport Nutr Exerc Metab. 2002 Mar;12(1):105-19.

400. Effects of glycerol-induced hyperhydration prior to exercise in the heat on sweating and core temperature. Lyons TP, Riedesel ML, Meuli LE, Chick TW. Med Sci Sports Exerc. 1990 Aug;22(4):477-83

401. Glycerol hyperhydration improves cycle time trial performance in hot humid conditions. Hitchins S, Martin DT, Burke L, Yates K, Fallon K, Hahn A, Dobson GP. Eur J Appl Physiol Occup Physiol. 1999 Oct;80(5):494-501.

402. Hyperhydration and glycerol: thermoregulatory effects during exercise in hot climates. Latzka WA, Sawka MN.

Can J Appl Physiol. 2000 Dec;25(6):536-45.

403. Cerebral dehydration action of glycerol. Tourtellotte WW et al. Clin Pharmacol Ther 13: 159-171, 1972.

404. The effect of glycerol hyperhydration on olympic distance triathlon performance in high ambient temperatures. Coutts A, Reaburn P, Mummery K, Holmes M. Int J Sport Nutr Exerc Metab. 2002 Mar;12(1):105-19

405. Hyperhydration: thermoregulatory effects during compensable exercise-heat stress. Latzka WA, Sawka MN, Montain SJ, Skrinar GS, Fielding RA, Matott RP, Pandolf KB. J Appl Physiol. 1997 Sep;83(3):860-6.

406. Hyperhydration: tolerance and cardiovascular effects during uncompensable exercise-heat stress. Latzka WA, Sawka MN, Montain SJ, Skrinar GS, Fielding RA, Matott RP, Pandolf KB. J Appl Physiol. 1998 Jun;84(6):1858-64.

407. The ergogenic potential of arginine. B. Campbell, P. La Bounty, M. Roberts. JISSN 1(2):35-38 (2004)

408. The effects of short-term alpha-ketoisocaproic acid supplementation on exercise performance: a randomized controlled trial. Yarrow JF, Parr JJ, White LJ, Borsa PA, Stevens BR. J Int Soc Sports Nutr. 2007 Jul 13;4:2.

409. High-intensity dynamic human muscle performance enhanced by a metabolic intervention. Stevens BR, Godfrey MD, Kaminski TW, Braith RW. Med Sci Sports Exerc. 2000 Dec;32(12):2102-8

410. Glycine-arginine-alpha-ketoisocaproic acid improves performance of repeated cycling sprints. Buford BN, Koch AJ. Med Sci Sports Exerc. 2004 Apr;36(4):583-7.

411. Propionyl-L-carnitine dilates human subcutaneous arteries through an endothelium-dependent mechanism. Cipolla MJ, Nicoloff A, Rebello T, Amato A, Porter JM. J Vasc Surg. 1999 Jun;29(6):1097-103.

412. Is glycine effective against elevated blood pressure? Hafidi ME et al. Curr Opin Clin Nutr Metab Care 2006, 9:26-31

413. Therapeutic Effects of L-Carnitine and Propionyl-L-carnitine on Cardiovascular Diseases: A Review. Roberto Ferrari, E. et al. Ann. N.Y. Acad. Sci. 1033: 79–91 (2004)

414. Propionyl-L-carnitine. Wiseman LR, Brogden RN. Drugs Aging. 1998 Mar;12(3):243-8; discussion 249-50.

415. Ergogenic effect of glycine and niacin separately and in combination. Hilsendager D, Karpovich PV. Res Q. 1964 Oct;35:SUPPL:389-92.

416. Glycine propionyl-L-carnitine produces enhanced anaerobic work capacity with reduced lactate accumulation in resistance trained males. Patrick L Jacobs. et al. Journal of the International Society of Sports Nutrition 2009, 6:9

417. Effect of glycine propionyl-L-carnitine on aerobic and anaerobic exercise performance. Smith WA, Fry AC, Tschume LC, Bloomer RJ. Int J Sport Nutr Exerc Metab. 2008 Feb;18(1):19-36.

418. Glycine propionyl-L-carnitine increases plasma nitrate/nitrite in resistance trained men. Bloomer RJ, Smith WA, Fisher-Wellman KH. J Int Soc Sports Nutr. 2007 Dec 3;4:22.

419. Effects of excess dietary leucine and leucine catabolites on growth and immune responses in weaning pigs. Gatnau, R et al. J. Anim. Sci. 73(1): 159-65.

420. Mechanism of attenuation by beta-hydroxy-beta-methylbutyrate of muscle protein degradation induced by lipopolysaccharide. Russell ST, Tisdale MJ. Mol Cell Biochem. 2009 Apr 30. [Epub ahead of print]

421. Beta-hydroxy-beta-methylbutyrate (HMB) stimulates myogenic cell proliferation, differentiation and survival via the MAPK/ERK and PI3K/Akt pathways. Kornasio R. et al. Biochem Biophys Acta. 2009 Jan 3 [epub].

422. Effect of beta-hydroxy-beta-methylbutyrate (HMB) on protein metabolism in whole body and in selected tissues. Holecek M, Muthny T, Kovarik M, Sispera L. Food Chem Toxicol. 2009 Jan;47(1):255-9. Epub 2008 Nov 21.

423. Effects of beta-hydroxy-beta-methylbutyrate on muscle damage after a prolonged run. Knitter AE, Panton L, Rathmacher JA, Petersen A, Sharp R. J Appl Physiol. 2000 Oct;89(4):1340-4.

424. Effects of nine weeks of beta-hydroxy-beta- methylbutyrate supplementation on strength and body composition in resistance trained men. Thomson JS, Watson PE, Rowlands DS. J Strength Cond Res. 2009 May;23(3):827-35.

425. Effects of beta-hydroxy-beta-methylbutyrate supplementation during resistance training on strength, body composition, and muscle damage in trained and untrained young men: a meta-analysis. Rowlands DS, Thomson JS. J Strength Cond Res. 2009 May;23(3):836-46.

426. Effects of ß-hydroxy-ß-methylbutyrate (HMB) on aerobic performance components and body composition in college students. Lamboley, C.R., D. Royer, and I.J. Dionne. Int. J. Sport Nutr. Exerc. Metab. 17:56-69 (2007)

427. Effects of icariin on cGMP-specific PDE5 and cAMP-specific PDE4 activities. Xin ZC, Kim EK, Lin CS, Liu WJ, Tian L, Yuan YM, Fu J. Asian J Androl. 2003 Mar;5(1):15-8.

428. Effect of icariin on cyclic GMP levels and on the mRNA expression of cGMP-binding cGMP-specific phosphodiesterase (PDE5) in penile cavernosum. Jiang Z, Hu B, Wang J, Tang Q, Tan Y, Xiang J, Liu J. J Huazhong Univ Sci Technolog Med Sci. 2006;26(4):460-2.

429. Effects of icariin on hypothalamic-pituitary-adrenal axis action and cytokine levels in stressed Sprague-Dawley rats. Pan Y, Zhang WY, Xia X, Kong LD. Biol Pharm Bull. 2006 Dec;29(12):2399-403.

430. Protective effects of icariin against learning and memory deficits induced by aluminium in rats. Luo Y, Nie J, Gong QH, Lu YF, Wu Q, Shi JS. Clin Exp Pharmacol Physiol. 2007 Aug;34(8):792-5.

431. Icariin, a flavonoid from the herb Epimedium enhances the osteogenic differentiation of rat primary bone marrow stromal cells. Chen KM, Ge BF, Ma HP, Liu XY, Bai MH, Wang Y. Pharmazie. 2005 Dec;60(12):939-42.

432. Standardization and evaluation of botanical mixtures: lessons from a traditional Chinese herb, Epimedium, with oestrogenic properties. Yong EL, Wong SP, Shen P, Gong YH, Li J, Hong Y. Novartis Found Symp. 2007;282:173-88; discussion 188-91, 212-8.

433. Determination of rat urinary metabolites of icariin in vivo and estrogenic activities of its metabolites on MCF-7 cells. Liu J, Ye H, Lou Y. Pharmazie. 2005 Feb;60(2):120-5.

434. Effects of icariin on erectile function and expression of nitric oxide synthase isoforms in castrated rats. Liu WJ, Xin ZC, Xin H, Yuan YM, Tian L, Guo YL. Asian J Androl. 2005 Dec;7(4):381-8.

435. Effects of yang-restoring herb medicines on the levels of plasma corticosterone, testosterone and triiodothyronine. Kuang AK, Chen JL, Chen MD. Zhong Xi Yi Jie He Za Zhi. 1989 Dec;9(12):737-8, 710.

436. A new herbal combination, Etana, for enhancing erectile function: an efficacy and safety study in animals. Qinna N, Taha H, Matalka KZ, Badwan AA. Int J Impot Res. 2009 Jun 4. [Epub ahead of print]

437. Ipriflavone, a synthetic phytoestrogen, enhances intestinal calcium transport in vitro. Arjmandi BH, Khalil DA, Hollis BW. Calcif Tissue Int. 2000 Sep;67(3):225-9.

438. Ipriflavone. Kitatani K, Morii H. Nippon Rinsho. 1998 Jun;56(6):1537-43.

439. Overview of clinical studies with ipriflavone. Attila BK. Acta Pharm Hung. 1995 Nov;65(6):223-8. Review.

440. Anabolic-weight-gain promoting compositions containing isoflavone derivatives and method using same. 1974. Feuer, L. U.S. Patent # 4,163,746.

441. Feuer L, Farkas L, Nogradi M, et al. Metabolic 5-methyl-isoflavone-derivatives, process for the preparation thereof and compositions containing the same. United States Patent 4,163,746, August 7, 1979.

442. Ipriflavone modulates IGF-I but is unable to restore bone in rats. Deyhim F, Smith BJ, Soung DY, Juma S, Devareddy L, Arjmandi BH. Phytother Res. 2005 Feb;19(2):116-20.

443. Efficacy of ipriflavone in established osteoporosis and long-term safety. Agnusdei D, Bufalino L. Calcif Tissue Int. 1997;61 Suppl 1:S23-7.

444. Dietary Protein Impact on Glycemic Control during Weight Loss. Donald K. Layman and Jamie I. Baum. J. Nutr. 134: 968S–973S, 2004

445. Leucine stimulates translation initiation in skeletal muscle of postabsorptive rats via a rapamycin-sensitive pathway. Anthony JC, Yoshizawa F, Anthony TG, Vary TC, Jefferson LS, Kimball SR. J Nutr. 2000 Oct;130(10):2413-9.

446. Leucine-enriched essential amino acid and carbohydrate ingestion following resistance exercise enhances mTOR signaling and protein synthesis in human muscle. Dreyer HC, Drummond MJ, Pennings B, Fujita S, Glynn EL, Chinkes DL, Dhanani S, Volpi E, Rasmussen BB. Am J Physiol Endocrinol Metab. 2008 Feb;294(2):E392-400. Epub 2007 Dec 4.

447. Leucine regulates translation initiation of protein synthesis in skeletal muscle after exercise. Norton LE, Layman DK. J Nutr. 2006 Feb;136(2):533S-537S.

448. Role of leucine in protein metabolism during exercise and recovery. Layman DK. Can J Appl Physiol. 2002 Dec;27(6):646-63.

449. Relationship between leucine oxidation and oxygen consumption during steady-state exercise. Lamont LS, McCullough AJ, Kalhan SC. Med Sci Sports Exerc. 2001 Feb;33(2):237-41.

450. The effects of BCAA and leucine supplementation and lower-body resistance exercise on the ERK 1/2 MAPK pathway signal transduction. Bill Campbell et al. JISSN 2008, 5 (Suppl 1): P19

451. Effects of dietary leucine supplementation on exercise performance. Crowe MJ, Weatherson JN, Bowden BF. Eur J Appl Physiol. 2006 Aug;97(6):664-72. Epub 2005 Oct 29.

452. Combined ingestion of protein and free leucine with carbohydrate increases postexercise muscle protein synthesis in vivo in male subjects. Rene´ Koopman et al. Am J Physiol Endocrinol Metab 288: E645–E653, 2005.

453. Leucine supplementation does not enhance acute strength or running performance but affects serum amino acid concentration. Pitkänen HT, Oja SS, Rusko H, Nummela A, Komi PV, Saransaari P, Takala T, Mero AA. Amino Acids. 2003 Jul;25(1):85-94.

454. Leucine supplementation and intensive training. Mero A. Sports Med. 1999 Jun;27(6):347-58. Review.

455. Stimulation of muscle anabolism by resistance exercise and ingestion of leucine plus protein. Tipton KD, Elliott TA, Ferrando AA, Aarsland AA, Wolfe RR. Appl Physiol Nutr Metab. 2009 Apr;34(2):151-61.

456. Effects of Eurycoma longifolia Jack (Tongkat Ali) on the initiation of sexual performance of inexperienced castrated male rats. Ang HH, Cheang HS, Yusof AP. Exp Anim. 2000 Jan;49(1):35-8.

457. Evaluation of the potency activity of aphrodisiac in Eurycoma longifolia Jack. Ang HH, Ikeda S, Gan EK. Phytother Res. 2001 Aug;15(5):435-6.

458. Cytotoxic and antimalarial constituents from the roots of Eurycoma longifolia. Kuo PC, Damu AG, Lee KH, Wu TS. Bioorg Med Chem. 2004 Feb 1;12(3):537-44.

459. Biologically Active Quassinoids and Their Chemistry: Potential Leads for Drug Design Z. Guo1, S. Vangapandu et al. Current Medicinal Chemistry, 2005, 12, 173-190 173

460. The ergogenic effects of Eurycoma longifolia Jack: A Pilot Study. S. Hamzah et al. 2003;37;464-470 Br. J. Sports Med.

461. Effect of Eurycoma longifolia Extract on Anabolic Balance During Endurance Exercise. Talbott S, et al. Journal of the International Society of Sports Nutrition. 3 (1)S1-S29, 2006

462. Anabolic-weight-gain promoting compositions containing isoflavone derivatives and method using same. 1974. Feuer, L. U.S. Patent # 4,163,746.

463. Feuer L, Farkas L, Nogradi M, et al. Metabolic 5-methyl-isoflavone-derivatives, process for the preparation thereof and compositions containing the same. United States Patent 4,163,746, August 7, 1979.

464. The effects of 5-methyl-7-methoxyisoflavone on body composition and performance in college-aged men. Incledon, Thomas, Van Gammeren, Darin1, Antonio, Jose, Medicine & Science in Sports & Exercise:Volume 33(5) Supplement 1May 2001p S338

465. Effects of methoxyisoflavone, ecdysterone, and sulfo-polysaccharide supplementation on training adaptations in

resistance-trained males. Wilborn CD, Taylor LW, Campbell BI, Kerksick C, Rasmussen CJ, Greenwood M, Kreider RB. J Int Soc Sports Nutr. 2006 Dec 13;3:19-27.

466. N-acetyl-L-Cysteine Promotes T Cell Mediated Immunity In Allogeneic Settings IN VIVO And IN VITRO. H. Karlsson, S. Nava, M. Remberger, Z. Hassan, M. Hassan, O. Ringden Biology of Blood and Marrow Transplantation, Volume 15, Issue 2, Pages 127-127

467. The comparison of antioxidant and haematological properties of N-acetylcysteine and alpha-lipoic acid in physically active males. Zembron-Lacny A, Slowinska-Lisowska M, Szygula Z, Witkowski K, Szyszka K. Physiol Res. 2008 Dec 17.

468. Effects of N-acetylcysteine on respiratory muscle fatigue during heavy exercise. Kelly MK, Wicker RJ, Barstow TJ, Harms CA. Respir Physiol Neurobiol. 2009 Jan 1;165(1):67-72. Epub 2008 Oct 17.

469. Effect of respiratory muscle fatigue on subsequent exercise performance. Mador MJ, Acevedo FA. J Appl Physiol. 1991 May;70(5):2059-65.

470. N-acetylcysteine enhances muscle cysteine and glutathione availability and attenuates fatigue during prolonged exercise in endurance-trained individuals. Medved I, Brown MJ, Bjorksten AR, Murphy KT, Petersen AC, Sostaric S, Gong X, McKenna MJ. J Appl Physiol. 2004 Oct;97(4):1477-85. Epub 2004 Jun 11

471. Effects of N-acetylcysteine on glutathione oxidation and fatigue during handgrip exercise. Matuszczak Y, Farid M, Jones J, Lansdowne S, Smith MA, Taylor AA, Reid MB. Muscle Nerve. 2005 Nov;32(5):633-8.

472. N-acetylcysteine inhibits muscle fatigue in humans. Reid MB, Stokiç DS, Koch SM, Khawli FA, Leis AA. J Clin Invest. 1994 Dec;94(6):2468-74.

473. N-acetylcysteine attenuates the decline in muscle Na+,K+-pump activity and delays fatigue during prolonged exercise in humans. McKenna MJ, Medved I, Goodman CA, Brown MJ, Bjorksten AR, Murphy KT, Petersen AC, Sostaric S, Gong X. J Physiol. 2006 Oct 1;576(Pt 1):279-88. Epub 2006 Jul 13.

474. The Healing Power of Rainforest Herbs. Leslie Taylor. (2005)

475. Lignans from the roots of Urtica dioica and their metabolites bind to human sex hormone binding globulin (SHBG). Schöttner M, Gansser D, Spiteller G. Planta Med. 1997 Dec;63(6):529-32.

476. Urtica dioicafor Treatment of Benign Prostatic Hyperplasia: A Prospective, Randomized, Double-Blind, Placebo-Controlled, Crossover Study. Mohammad Reza Safarinejad. Journal Of Herbal Pharmacotherapy, 1522-9106, Volume 5, Issue 4, 2006, Pages 1–11

477. Phospholipids and sports performance. Jäger R, Purpura M, Kingsley M. J Int Soc Sports Nutr. 2007 Jul 25;4:5.

478. The effects of phosphatidylserine on endocrine response to moderate intensity exercise. Starks MA, Starks SL, Kingsley M, Purpura M, Jäger R. J Int Soc Sports Nutr. 2008 Jul 28;5:11.

479. Blunting by chronic phosphatidylserine administration of the stress-induced activation of the hypothalamo-pituitary-adrenal axis in healthy men. Monteleone P, Maj M, Beinat L, Natale M, Kemali D. Eur J Clin Pharmacol.

1992;42(4):385-8.

480. Effects of phosphatidylserine on exercise capacity during cycling in active males. Kingsley MI, Miller M, Kilduff LP, McEneny J, Benton D. Med Sci Sports Exerc. 2006 Jan;38(1):64-71.

481. Effects of phosphatidylserine on oxidative stress following intermittent running. Kingsley MI, Wadsworth D, Kilduff LP, McEneny J, Benton D. Med Sci Sports Exerc. 2005 Aug;37(8):1300-6.

482. The effects of phosphatidyl serine on markers of muscular stress in endurance runners. Fernholz KM et al. Med Sci Sport Exerc 2000, 32(5):s321.

483. The hormonal and perceptive effects of phosphatidylserine administration during two weeks of weight training-induced over-training. Fahey TD et al. Biol Sport 15(2):135-44 (1998)

484. The role of ribose in human skeletal muscle metabolism. Dodd SL, Johnson CA, Fernholz K, St Cyr JA. Med Hypotheses. 2004;62(5):819-24.

485. ATP breakdown products in human skeletal muscle during prolonged exercise to exhaustion. Norman B, Sollevi A, Kaijser L, Jansson E. Clin Physiol. 1987 Dec;7(6):503-10.

486. Energetics of human muscle: exercise-induced ATP depletion. Taylor DJ, Styles P, Matthews PM, Arnold DA, Gadian DG, Bore P, Radda GK. Magn Reson Med. 1986 Feb;3(1):44-54.

487. Effect of ribose supplementation on resynthesis of adenine nucleotides after intense intermittent training in humans. Hellsten Y, Skadhauge L, Bangsbo J. Am J Physiol Regul Integr Comp Physiol. 2004 Jan;286(1):R182-8.

488. The effects of four weeks of ribose supplementation on body composition and exercise performance in healthy young male recreational bodybuilders. Van Gammeren D et al. Curr Ther Res 63(8), 486-95 (2002)

489. Effects of oral D-ribose supplementation on anaerobic capacity and selected metabolic markers in healthy males. Kreider RB, Melton C, Greenwood M, Rasmussen C, Lundberg J, Earnest C, Almada A. Int J Sport Nutr Exerc Metab. 2003 Mar;13(1):76-86.

490. Effects of ribose supplementation on repeated sprint performance in men. Berardi JM, Ziegenfuss TN. J Strength Cond Res. 2003 Feb;17(1):47-52.

491. Assessment of Hematological and Biochemical parameters with extended D-Ribose ingestion. Seifert J, Frelich A, Shecterle L, St Cyr J. J Int Soc Sports Nutr. 2008 Sep 15;5:13.

492. Contraceptives and other steroid drugs: their production from steroidal sapogenins.Fazli FR. Pak J Sci. 1968 Jan-Mar;20(1 and 2):64-7.

493. The biological action of saponins in animal systems: a review. Francis G, Kerem Z, Makkar HP, Becker K. Br J Nutr. 2002 Dec;88(6):587-605.

494. The bioactivity of saponins: triterpenoid and steroidal lycosides. Rao AV. Gurfinkel DM. Drug Metab Drug Interact 2000;17(1-4):211-35

495. Implication of steroid saponins and sapogenins in the hypocholesterolemic effect of fenugreek. Sauvaire Y, Ribes G, Baccou JC, Loubatieères-Mariani MM. Lipids. 1991 Mar;26(3):191-7.

496. Saponins: Properties, Applications and Processing. zlem Gl-stnda; Giuseppe Mazza. Critical Reviews in Food Science and Nutrition, Volume 47, Issue 3 March 2007 , pages 231 – 258

497. Antioxidative and hypolipidemic effects of diosgenin, a steroidal saponin of yam (Dioscorea spp.), on high-cholesterol fed rats. Son IS, Kim JH, Sohn HY, Son KH, Kim JS, Kwon CS. Biosci Biotechnol Biochem. 2007 Dec;71(12):3063-71. Epub 2007 Dec 7.

498. Cancer chemopreventive and therapeutic effects of diosgenin, a food saponin. Raju J, Mehta R. Nutr Cancer. 2009;61(1):27-35.

499. Diosgenin--a growth stimulator of mammary gland of ovariectomized mouse. Aradhana. Rao AR. Kale RK. (1992) Indian Journal of Experimental Biology, 30(5):367-70

500. Effects of wild yam extract on menopausal symptoms, lipids and sex hormones in healthy menopausal women. Komesaroff PA, Black CV, Cable V, Sudhir K. Climacteric. 2001 Jun;4(2):144-50.

501. Experimental study of the anabolic activity of 6-ketoderivatives of certain natural sapogenins. Syrov VN, Kurmukov AG. Farmakol Toksikol. 1976 Sep-Oct;39(5):631-5.

502. Induction of growth hormone release by dioscin from Dioscorea batatas DECNE. Lee HY, Jung DY, Ha H, Son KH, Jeon SJ, Kim C. J Biochem Mol Biol. 2007 Nov 30;40(6):1016-20.

503. Experimental study of the anabolic activity of 6-ketoderivatives of certain natural sapogenins. Syrov VN, Kurmukov AG. Farmakol Toksikol. 1976 Sep-Oct;39(5):631-5.

504. Effects of wild yam extract on menopausal symptoms, lipids and sex hormones in healthy menopausal women. Komesaroff PA, Black CV, Cable V, Sudhir K. Climacteric. 2001 Jun;4(2):144-50.

505. Sulfated polysaccharides of brown seaweed Cystoseira canariensis bind to serum myostatin protein. Ramazanov Z, Jimenez del Rio M, Ziegenfuss T. Acta Physiol Pharmacol Bulg. 2003;27(2-3):101-6.

506. Effects of an alleged myostatin-binding supplement and heavy resistance training on serum myostatin, muscle strength and mass, and body composition. Willoughby DS. Int J Sport Nutr Exerc Metab. 2004 Aug;14(4):461-72.

507. Effects of methoxyisoflavone, ecdysterone, and sulfo-polysaccharide supplementation on training adaptations in resistance-trained males. Wilborn CD, Taylor LW, Campbell BI, Kerksick C, Rasmussen CJ, Greenwood M, Kreider RB. J Int Soc Sports Nutr. 2006 Dec 13;3:19-27.

508. Sexual effects of puncturevine (Tribulus terrestris) extract (protodioscin): an evaluation using a rat model. Gauthaman K, Ganesan AP, Prasad RN. J Altern Complement Med. 2003 Apr;9(2):257-65.

509. Aphrodisiac properties of Tribulus Terrestris extract (Protodioscin) in normal and castrated rats. Gauthaman K, Adaikan PG, Prasad RN. Life Sci. 2002 Aug 9;71(12):1385-96.

510. The hormonal effects of Tribulus terrestris and its role in the management of male erectile dysfunction--an evaluation using primates, rabbit and rat. Gauthaman K, Ganesan AP. Phytomedicine. 2008 Jan;15(1-2):44-54.

511. Distribution of steroidal saponins in Tribulus terrestris from different geographical regions. Dinchev D, Janda B, Evstatieva L, Oleszek W, Aslani MR, Kostova I. Phytochemistry. 2008 Jan;69(1):176-86. Epub 2007 Aug 23.

512. Tribestan effect on the concentration of some hormones in the serum of healthy subjects S. Milanov, A. Maleeva, M. Taskov RIRR - Radioisotope and Radioimmunological Laboratory, Sofia

513. The hormonal effects of Tribulus terrestris and its role in the management of male erectile dysfunction--an evaluation using primates, rabbit and rat. Gauthaman K, Ganesan AP. Phytomedicine. 2008 Jan;15(1-2):44-54.

514. The aphrodisiac herb Tribulus terrestris does not influence the androgen production in young men. Neychev VK, Mitev VI. J Ethnopharmacol. 2005 Oct 3;101(1-3):319-23.

515. The effect of five weeks of Tribulus terrestris supplementation on muscle strength and body composition during preseason training in elite rugby league players. Rogerson S, Riches CJ, Jennings C, Weatherby RP, Meir RA, Marshall-Gradisnik SM. J Strength Cond Res. 2007 May;21(2):348-53.

516. The effects of Tribulus terrestris on body composition and exercise performance in resistance-trained males. Antonio J, Uelmen J, Rodriguez R, Earnest C. Int J Sport Nutr Exerc Metab. 2000 Jun;10(2):208-15.

517. Magnesium, zinc, and chromium nutriture and physical activity. Henry C Lukaski. Am J Clin Nutr2000;72(suppl):585S–93S

518. Vitamin B6 deficiency can reduce fuel storage and utilization in physically trained rats. Choi EY, Cho YO. Int J Vitam Nutr Res. 2008 Mar;78(2):64-9.

519. Effects of a Novel Zinc-Magnesium Formulation on Hormones and Strength L.R. Brilla and Victor Conte. Journal of Exercise Physiology (Online) Volume 3 Number 4 October 2000.

520. Serum testosterone and urinary excretion of steroid hormone metabolites after administration of a high-dose zinc supplement. K Koehler. Eur J Clin Nutr 63, 65-70 (2009)

521. Effects of Zinc Magnesium Aspartate (ZMA) Supplementation on Training Adaptations and Markers of Anabolism and Catabolism. Wilborn CD, Kerksick CM et al. J Int Soc Sports Nutr. 2004 Dec 31;1(2):12-20.